Workbook

Progress in Mathematics

SADLIER-OXFORD

Catherine D. LeTourneau

with

Elinor R. Ford

Sadlier-Oxford
A Division of William H. Sadlier, Inc.
www.sadlier-oxford.com

Contributing Illustrators: Bernard Adnet, Scott Angle, Sarah Beise, Richard Bernal, Mary Bono, Ken Bowser, Mircea Catusnu, Georgia Cawley, Liz Conrad, John Corkery, Bob Holt, Nathan Jarvis, Gary Johnson, Dave Jonason, Dean Macadam, Ariel Pang, P.T. Pie, Dan Sharp, Ken Spengler, Jackie Stafford, Blake Thornton, Gregg Valley, Dirk Wanderlich.

Contents

CHAPTER 1 Sorting

CHAPTER 2 Geometry and Patterns

CHAPTER 3 Positions

C Denotes Common Core lesson.

Numbers 0-10

Numbers to 31

Tables, Graphs, and Fractions

Addition Readiness

C Denotes Common Core lesson.

8 Subtraction Readiness

9 Money

10 Time

11 Measurement

12 Numbers to 100

C Denotes Common Core lesson.

Additional Common Core Contents

Follow Directions

Name _____

✗ the penguin.

Circle the bird.

✓ the bear.

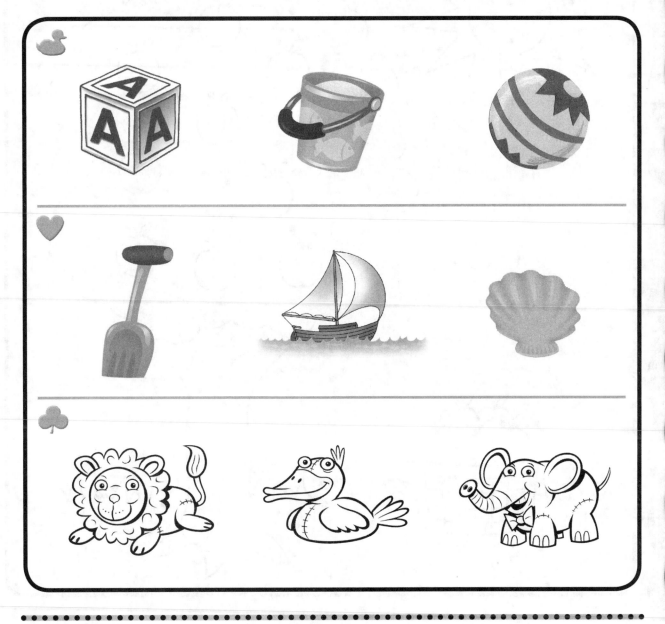

Directions

🦆 **✗** the pail.

♥ Circle the shovel.

♣ **✓** the elephant.

Color Recognition

Name _____

red   blue   yellow   green

Directions

Color the sun yellow. Color the sky blue.
Color the apples on the tree red. Color
the apples in the basket green.

Ball, Box, Can

Name _____

Ball | Box | Can

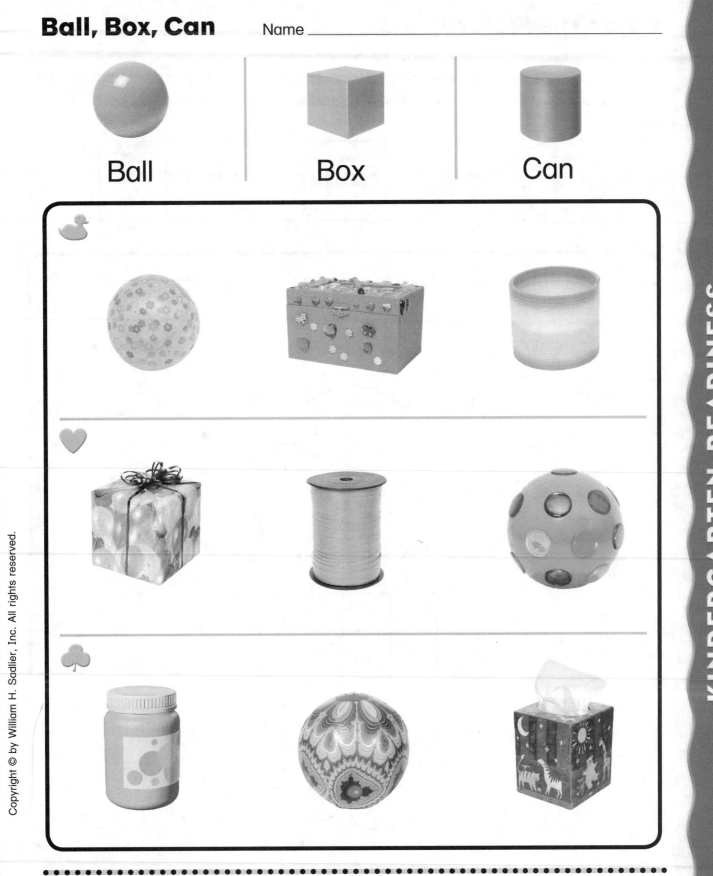

Directions

- ✗ the object shaped like a ball.
- Circle the object shaped like a can.
- ✓ the object shaped like a box.

3

Color The Picture

Name _____

red   blue   yellow

Directions

Color the robot juggler. Color the balls red.
Color the boxes blue. Color the cans yellow.

Matching

Name _____

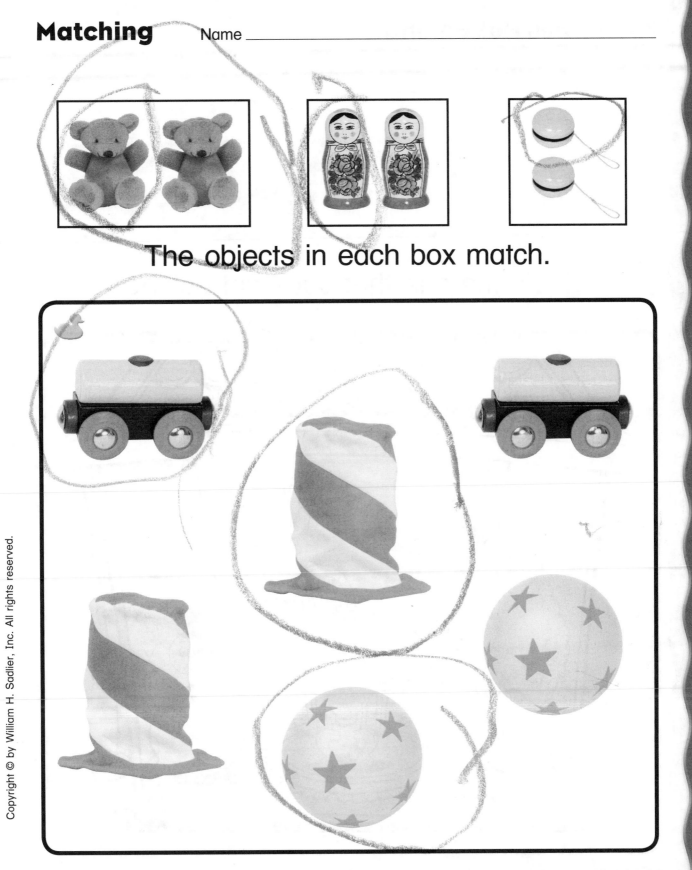

The objects in each box match.

KINDERGARTEN READINESS

Directions

Draw lines to show the objects that match.

5

What Does Not Belong?

Name _____

Circle the one that does not belong.

KINDERGARTEN READINESS

Directions

Look at the picture of the inside of the house.
Circle the objects that do not belong inside
the house. Then color the picture.

What Goes Together?

Name _____

Directions
Circle the objects that go together.

Find the Number

Name _____

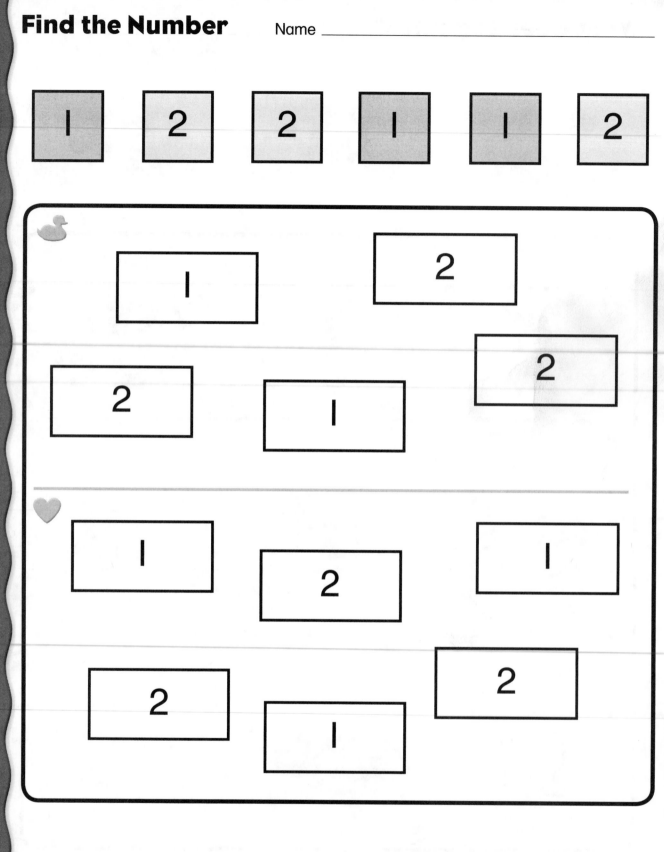

Directions

Color red the boxes with the number 1.

Color green the boxes with the number 2.

Alike/Same

Name _____

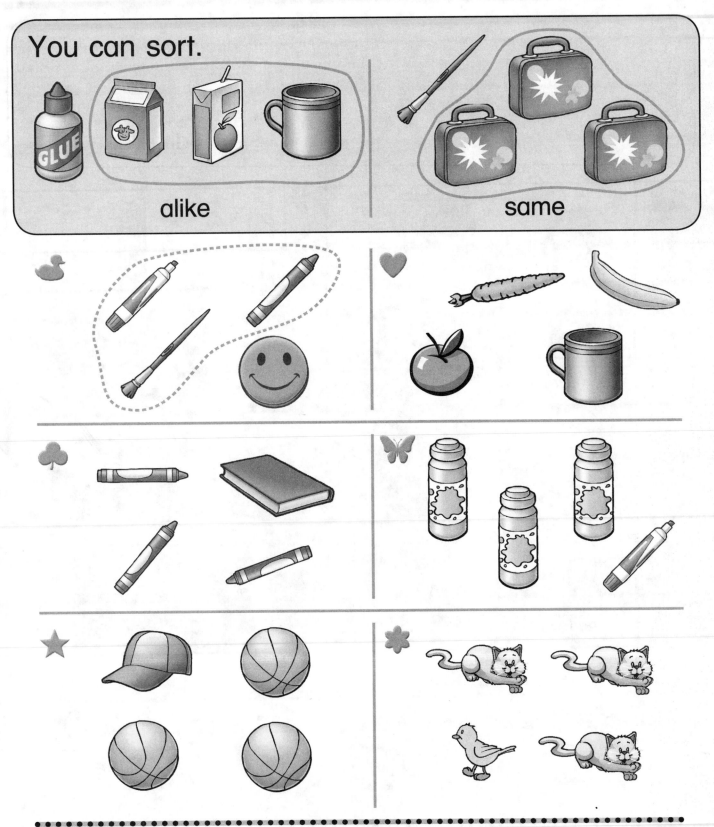

You can sort.

alike   same

Directions

Sort the objects. Circle the objects that are alike.

Sort the objects. Circle the objects that are the same.

C Use with Lesson 1-1, pages 3–4 in the Student Book.
C Then go to Lesson 1-2, pages 5–6 in the Student Book.

9

Different

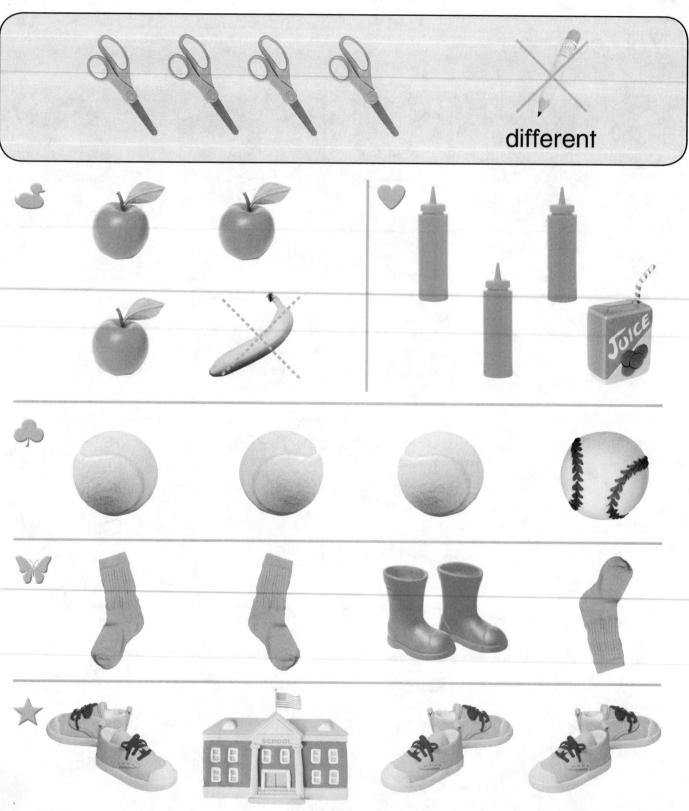

different

Directions

Sort the objects. Put an ✗ on the object that is different.

10

C Use with Lesson 1-2, pages 5–6 in the Student Book.
C Then go to Lesson 1-3, pages 7–8 in the Student Book.

Sort by Color

Sort by color.

same color

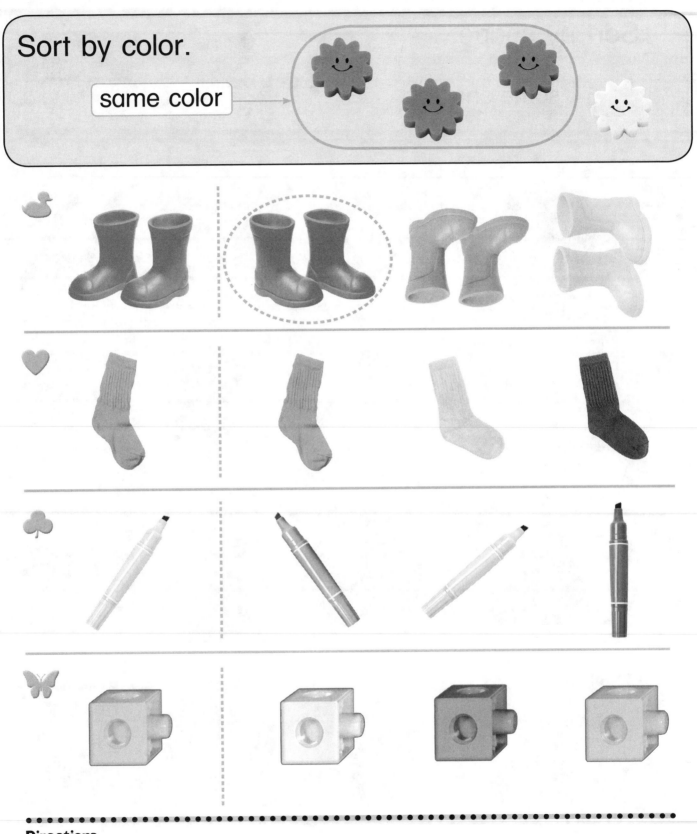

Directions

Circle the object that is the same color as the object at the beginning of the row.

C Use with Lesson 1-3, pages 7–7 in the Student Book.
C Then go to Lesson 1-4, pages 9–10 in the Student Book.

Same Shape

Name _____

Sort by shape.

same shape →

Directions

Circle the object that is shaped like the object at the beginning of the row.

Use with Lesson 1-4, pages 9–10 in the Student Book.
Then go to Lesson 1-5, pages 13–14 in the Student Book.

Sort by Size

Name _____

big   small

Directions

🦆 Circle the objects that are small in real life.
Put an ✗ on the objects that are big in real life.

C Use with Lesson 1-5, pages 13–14 in the Student Book.
C Then go to Lesson 1-6, pages 15–16 in the Student Book.

Sort by Color and Shape

Name _____

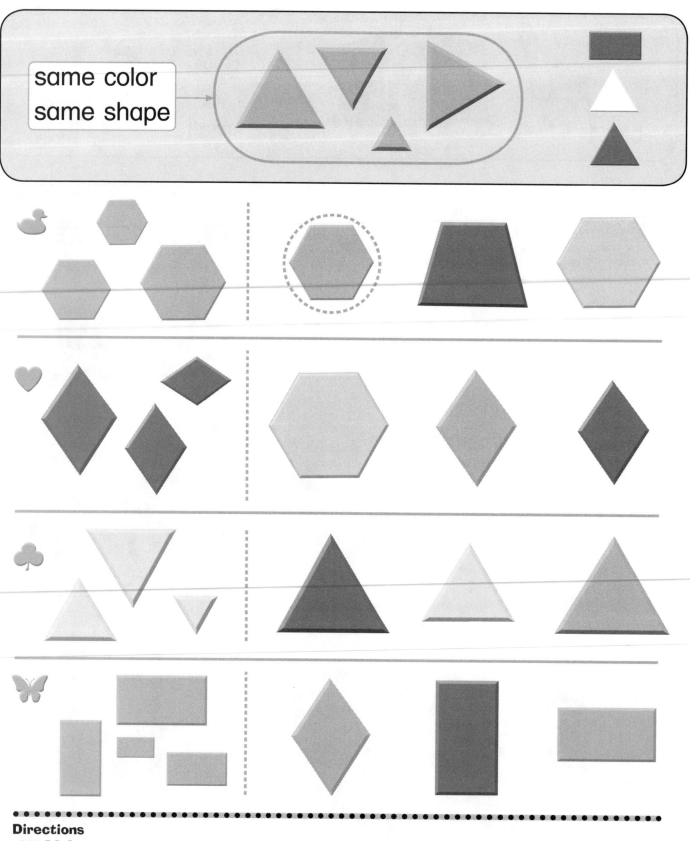

Directions

Circle the object that is the same shape and the same color as the group of objects at the beginning of the row.

14

C Use with Lesson 1-6, pages 15–16 in the Student Book.
C Then go to Lesson 1-7, pages 17–18 in the Student Book.

Sort by Shape and Size

Name _____

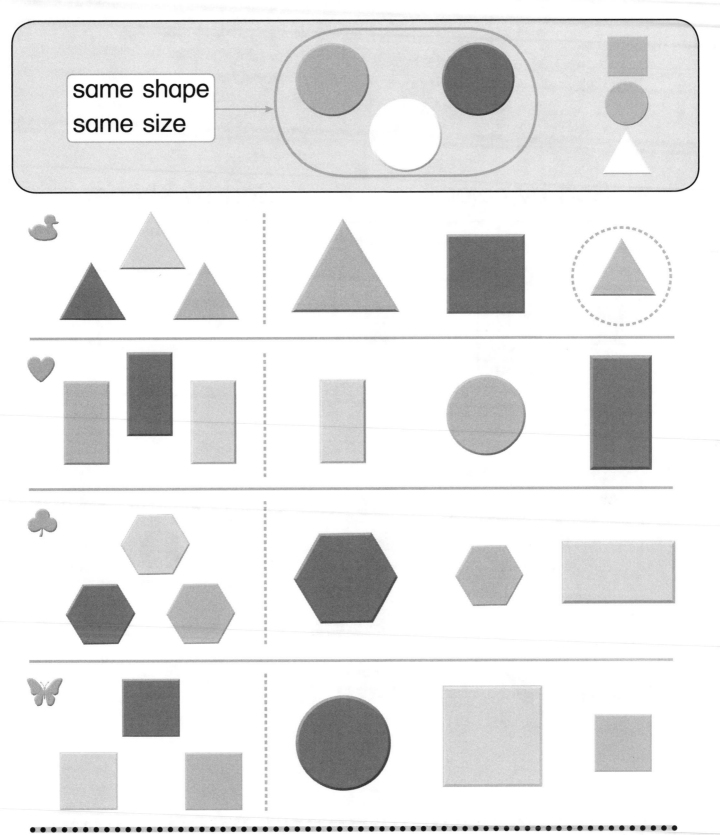

same shape
same size

Directions

🦆❤️♣️🦋 Circle the object that is the same shape and the same size as the group of objects at the beginning of the row.

C Use with Lesson 1-7, pages 17–18 in the Student Book.
C Then go to Lesson 1-8, pages 19–20 in the Student Book.

15

Sort Two Ways

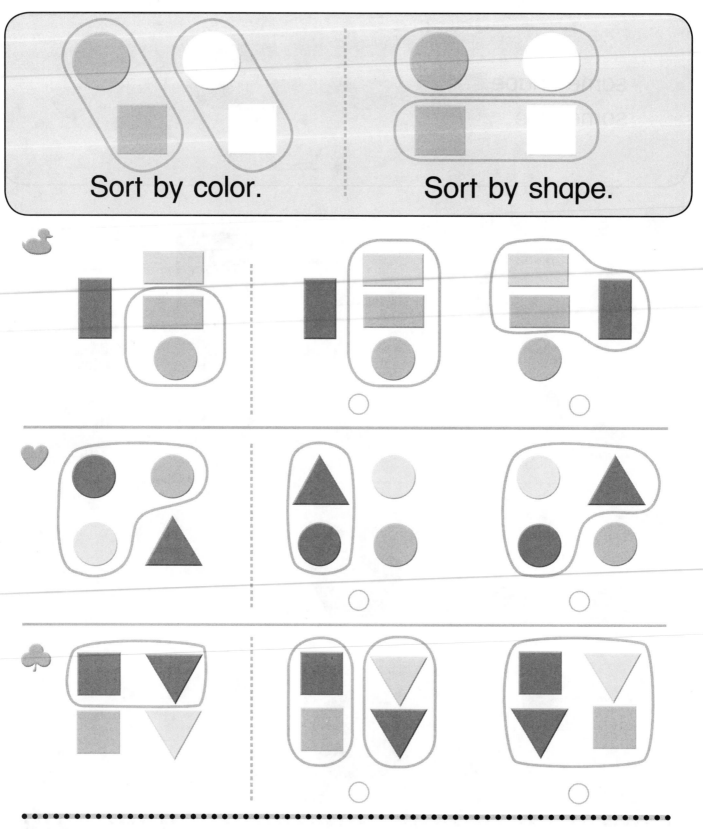

Sort by color.

Sort by shape.

Directions

🦆♥️♣️ Look at the way the group at the beginning of the row is
sorted. Fill in the circle under the group that is sorted
another way that makes sense.

C Use with Lesson 1-8, pages 19–20 in the Student Book.
C Then go to Lesson 1-9, pages 21–22 in the Student Book.

Problem-Solving Strategy: Logical Reasoning

Name _____

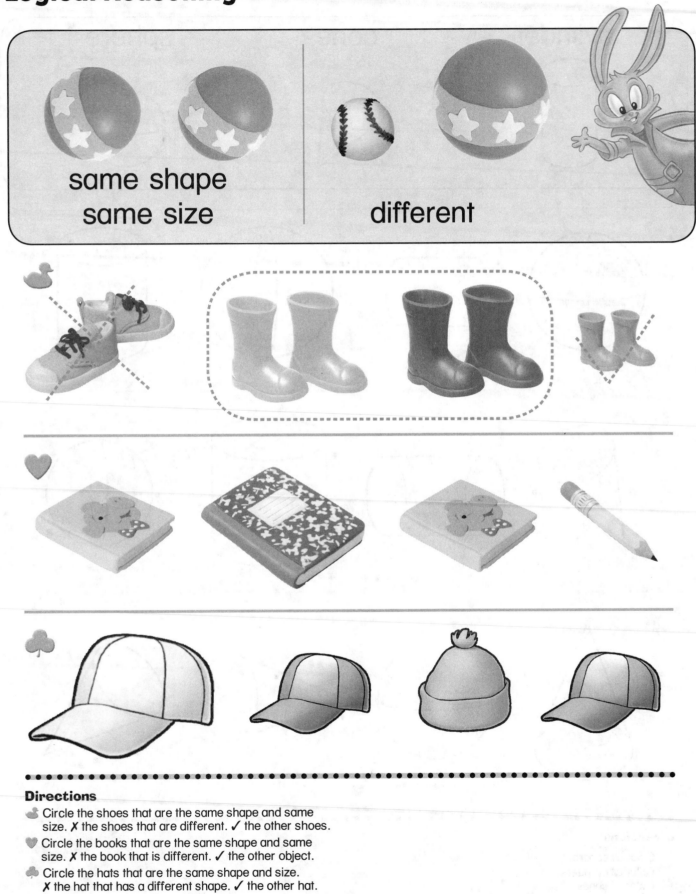

same shape
same size

different

Directions

🦆 Circle the shoes that are the same shape and same
size. ✗ the shoes that are different. ✓ the other shoes.

💜 Circle the books that are the same shape and same
size. ✗ the book that is different. ✓ the other object.

♣ Circle the hats that are the same shape and size.
✗ the hat that has a different shape. ✓ the other hat.

C Use with Lesson 1-9, pages 21–22 in the Student Book.

17

Cylinder, Cone, and Sphere

Name _____

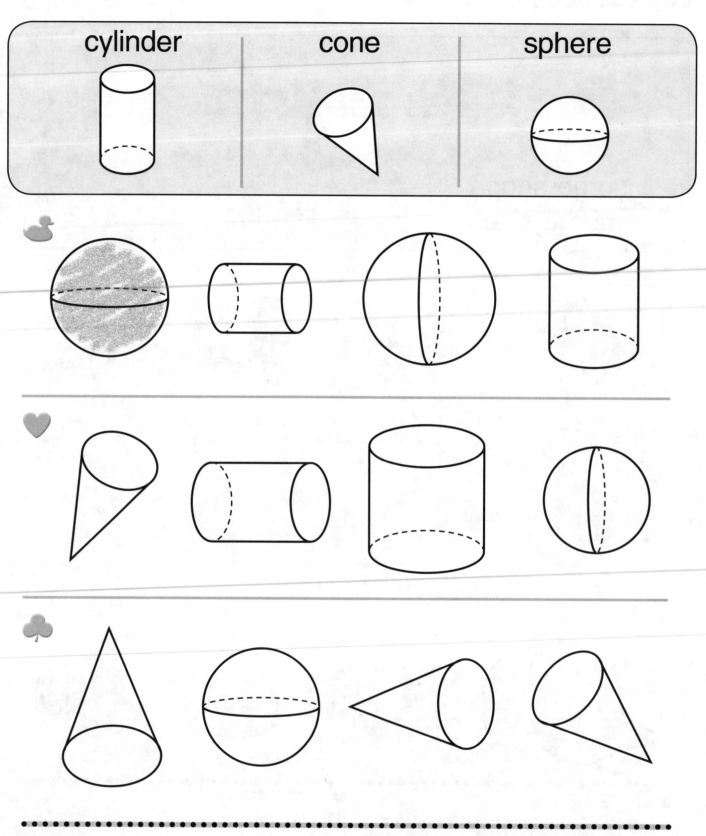

| cylinder | cone | sphere |

Directions
- Color all spheres.
- Color all cylinders.
- Color all cones.

Use with Lesson 2-1, pages 37–38 in the Student Book.
Then go to Lesson 2-2, pages 39–40 in the Student Book.

Cube and Rectangular Prism

Name _____

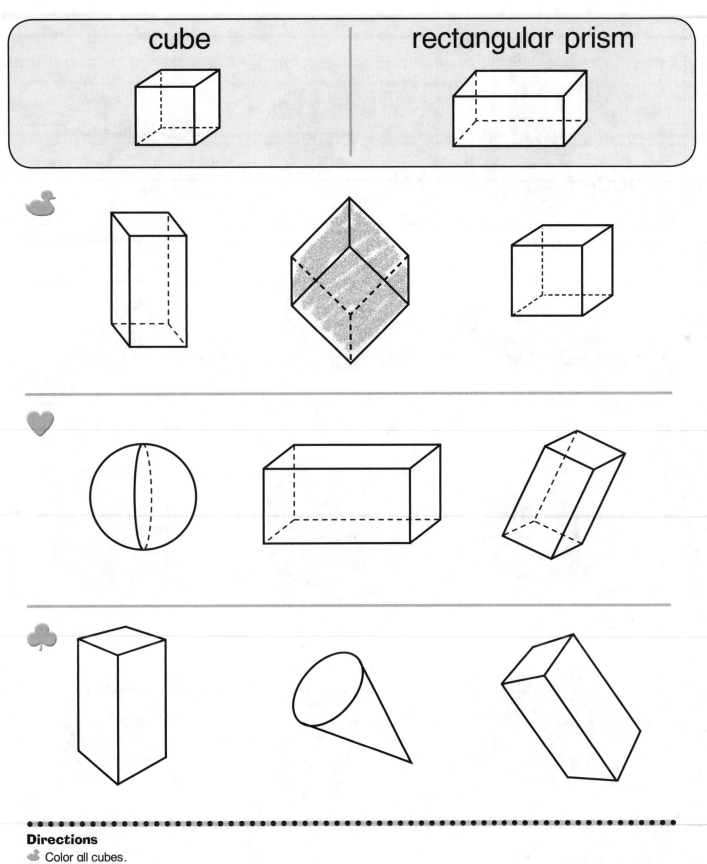

| cube | rectangular prism |

Directions
🦆 Color all cubes.
💜 ♣ Color all rectanglar prisms.

C Use with Lesson 2-2, pages 39–40 in the Student Book.
C Then go to Lesson 2-2A, pages 143–144 in this Workbook.

19

Moving Shapes

Name _____

stack · roll · slide

Directions
- Circle shapes that can roll.
- Circle shapes that can stack.
- Circle shapes that can slide.

20

Use with Lesson 2-3, pages 41–42 in the Student Book.
Then go to Lesson 2-4, pages 43–44 in the Student Book.

Plane Figures on Solids

Name _____

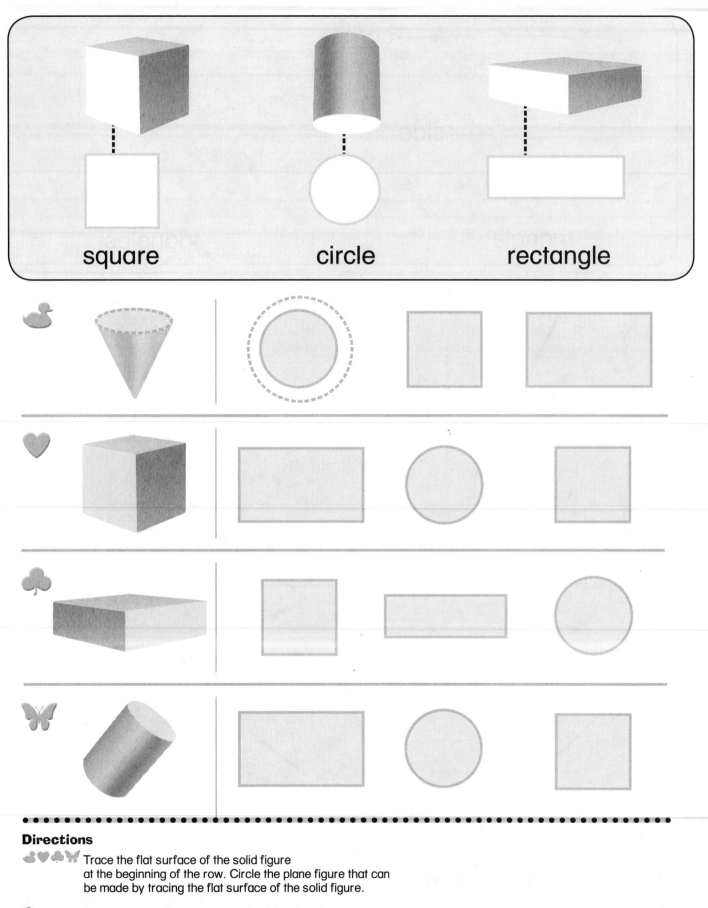

square   circle   rectangle

Directions

🦆💜♣🦋 Trace the flat surface of the solid figure
at the beginning of the row. Circle the plane figure that can
be made by tracing the flat surface of the solid figure.

C Use with Lesson 2-4, pages 43–44 in the Student Book.
C Then go to Lesson 2-4A, pages 145–146 in this Workbook.

21

Triangle

Name _____

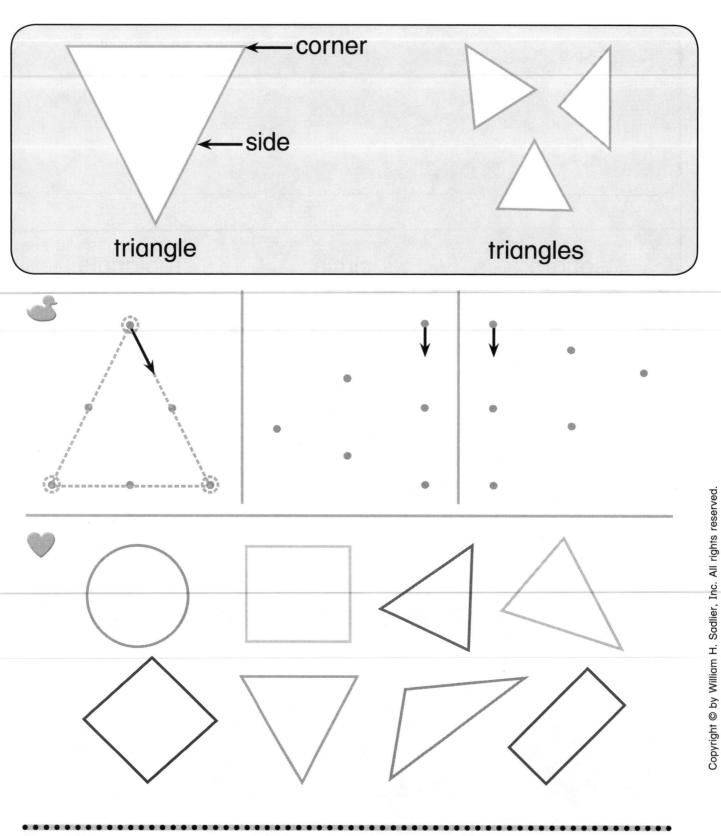

corner

side

triangle

triangles

Directions

🦆 Connect the dots to draw the sides of each triangle.
Circle the corners of each triangle.

💜 Color inside all of the shapes that are triangles.
Then circle their corners.

22

C Use with Lesson 2-5, pages 45–46 in the Student Book.
C Then go to Lesson 2-6, pages 47–48 in the Student Book.

Square and Rectangle

Name _____

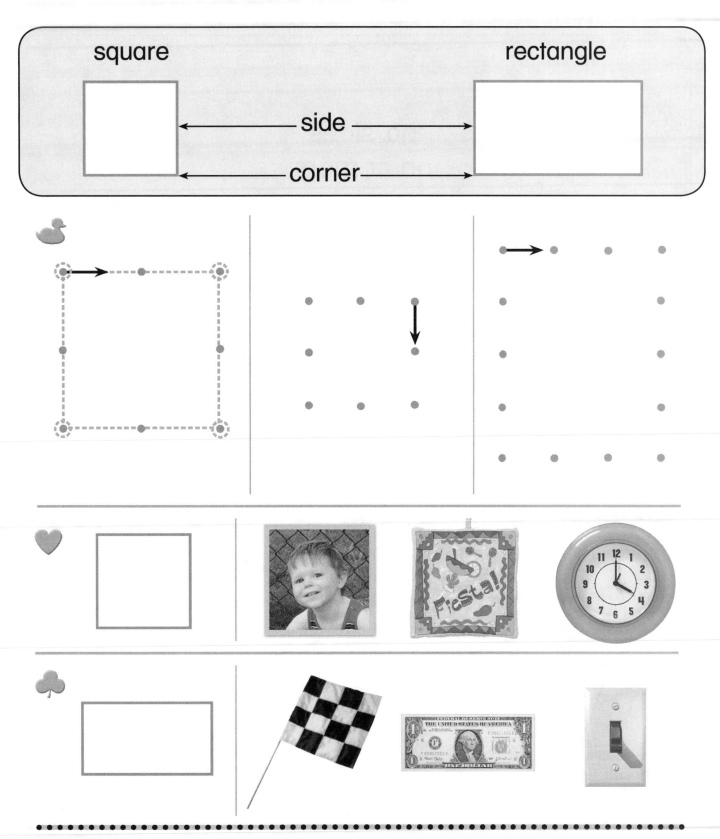

square   rectangle

side

corner

Directions

🦆 Connect the dots to draw the sides of each square or rectangle.
Circle the corners.

♥♣ Name the plane figure at the beginning of the row. Circle the objects
that are shaped like the plane figure at the beginning of each row.

Ⅽ Use with Lesson 2-6, pages 47–48 in the Student Book.
Ⅽ Then go to Lesson 2-7, pages 49–50 in the Student Book.

Circle

Name _____

no sides
no corners

circle   circle

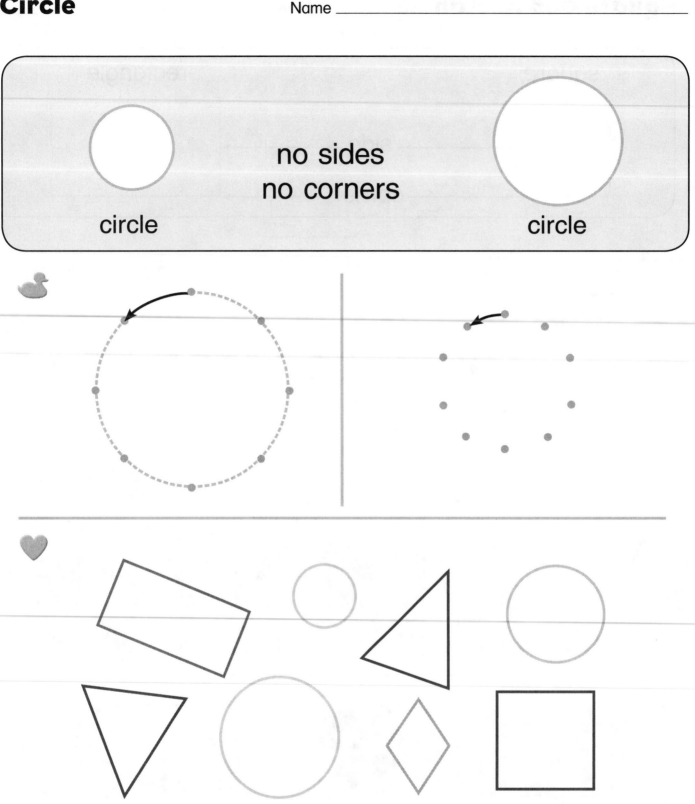

Directions

🦆 Follow the arrow and connect the dots to draw each circle.

♥ Color inside all the shapes that are circles.

24

C Use with Lesson 2-7, pages 49–50 in the Student Book.
C Then go to Lesson 2-7A, pages 147–148 in this Workbook.

Combine and Separate Figures

Name _____

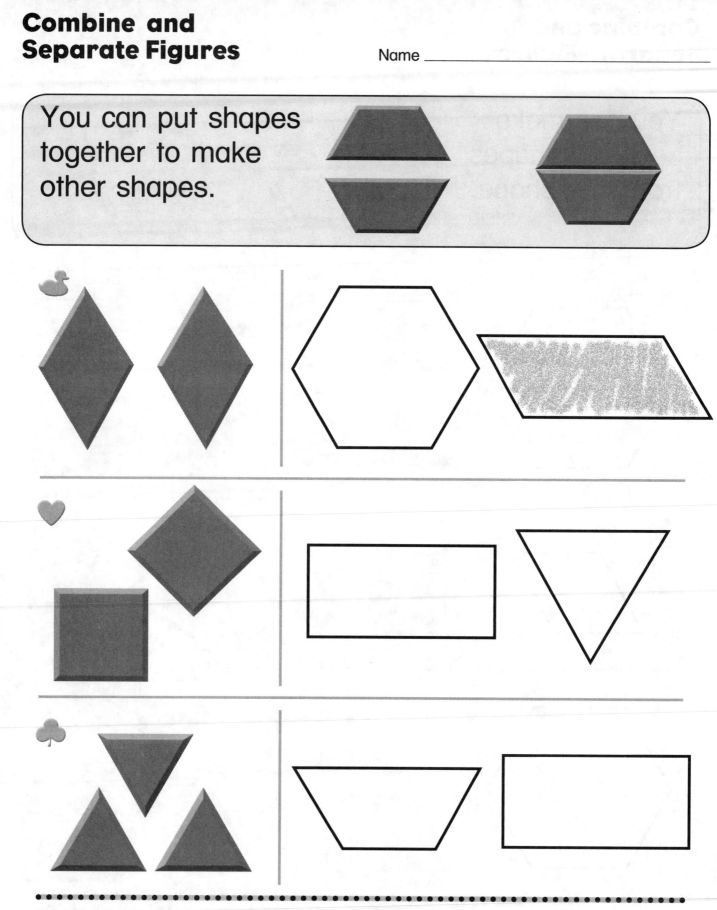

You can put shapes together to make other shapes.

••

Directions

🦆♥♣ Use pattern blocks of the shapes at the beginning of the row. Which shape in that row will all the blocks cover exactly? Trace and color to show your work.

C Use with Lesson 2-8, pages 51–52 in the Student Book.
C Then go to page 26 in this Workbook.

25

Combine and Separate Figures

Name _____

You can make separate shapes from one shape.

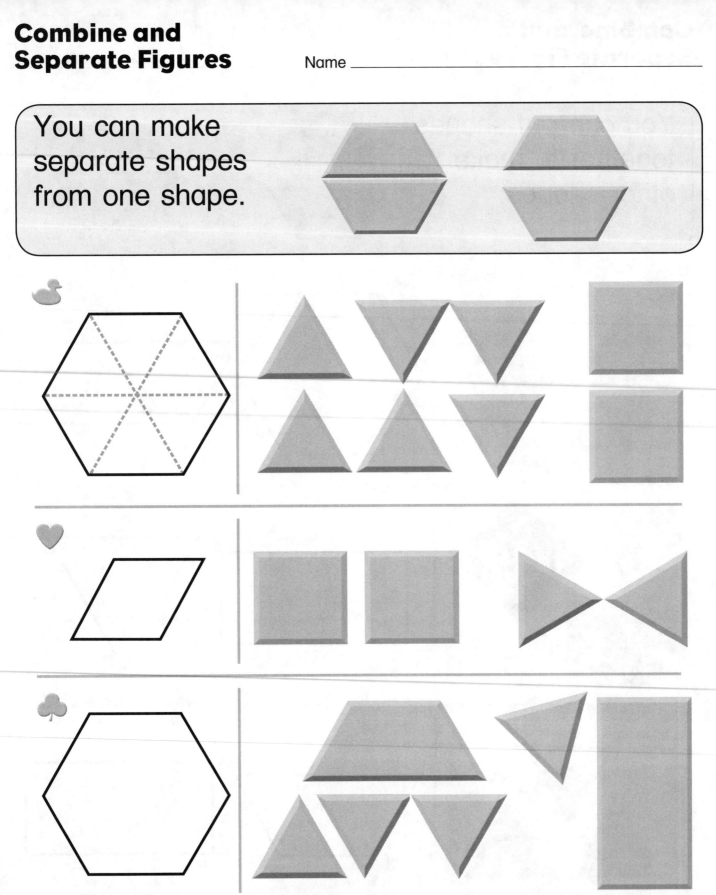

Directions

Use pattern blocks of the shape at the beginning of the row. Which group of shapes in that row can you make from the shape at the beginning of the row? Use pattern blocks of the group of smaller shapes to find out. Circle the group of shapes you use.

Use with Lesson 2-8, pages 51–52 in the Student Book.
Then go to Lesson 2-9, pages 55–56 in the Student Book.

Color Patterns

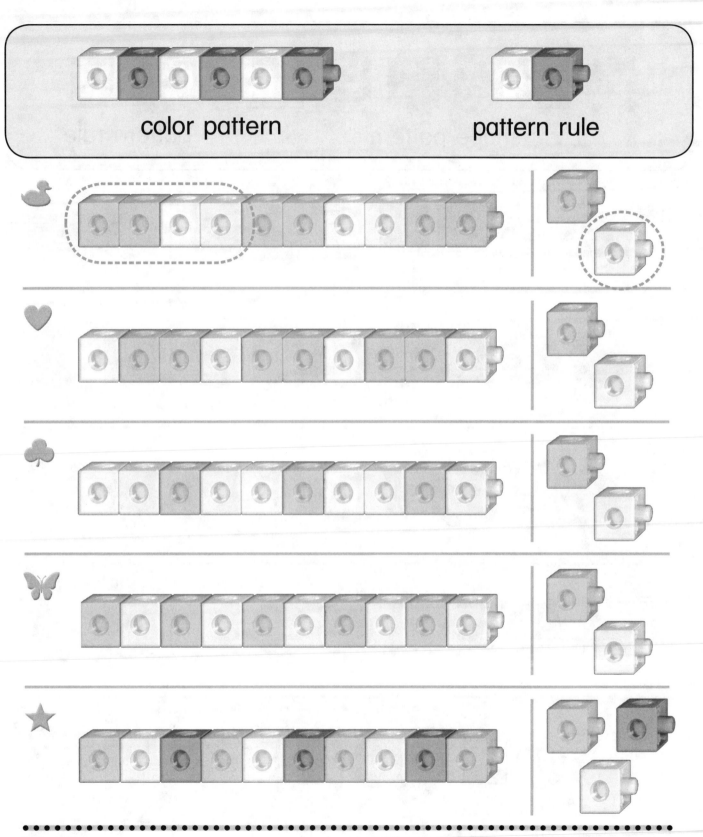

color pattern

pattern rule

Directions

🦆💜♣🦋⭐ Look for a color pattern. Circle the pattern rule. Circle the object that is most likely to come next.

Use with Lesson 2-9, pages 55–56 in the Student Book.
Then go to Lesson 2-10, pages 57–58 in the Student Book.

Shape Patterns

Name _____

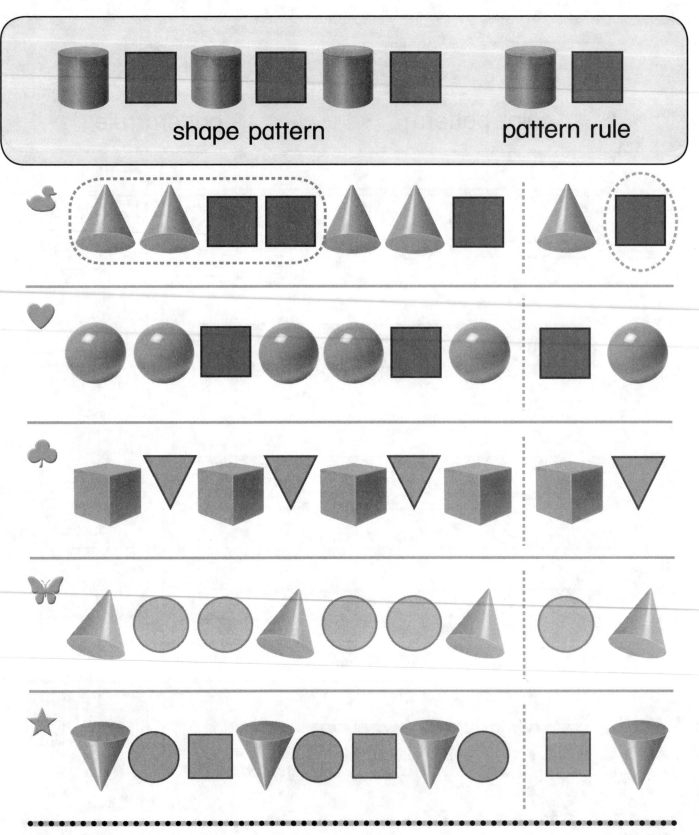

shape pattern   pattern rule

Directions

Look for a shape pattern. Circle the pattern rule. Circle the shape at the end of the row that is most likely to come next.

Use with Lesson 2-10, pages 57–58 in the Student Book.
Then go to Lesson 2-11, pages 59–60 in the Student Book.

Size and Growing Patterns

Name _____

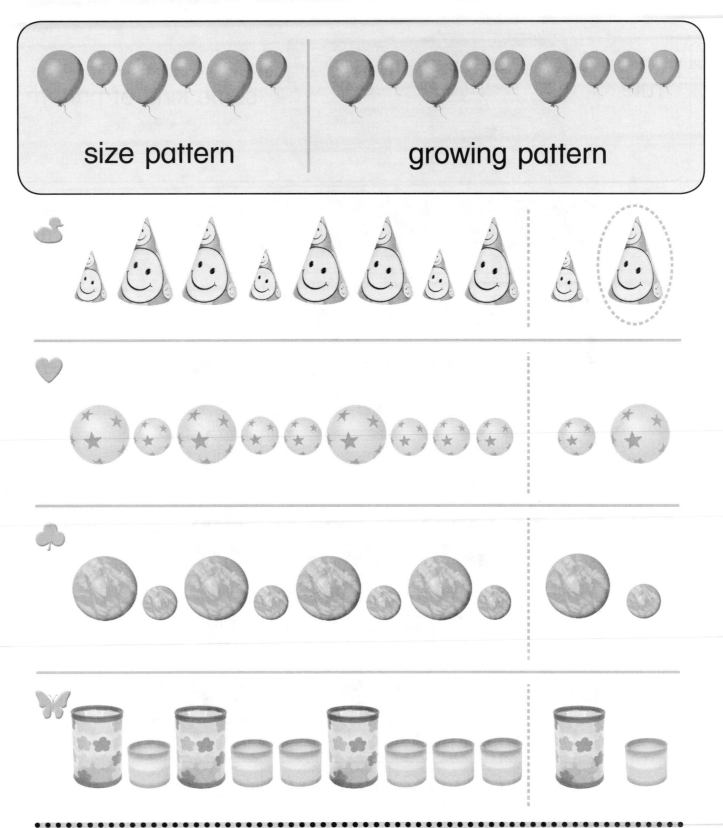

size pattern | growing pattern

Directions

🦆💗♣🦋 Look for a size or growing pattern. Circle the object at
the end of the row that is most likely to come next.

C Use with Lesson 2-11, pages 59–60 in the Student Book.
   Then go to Lesson 2-12, pages 61–62 in the Student Book.

Transfer Patterns

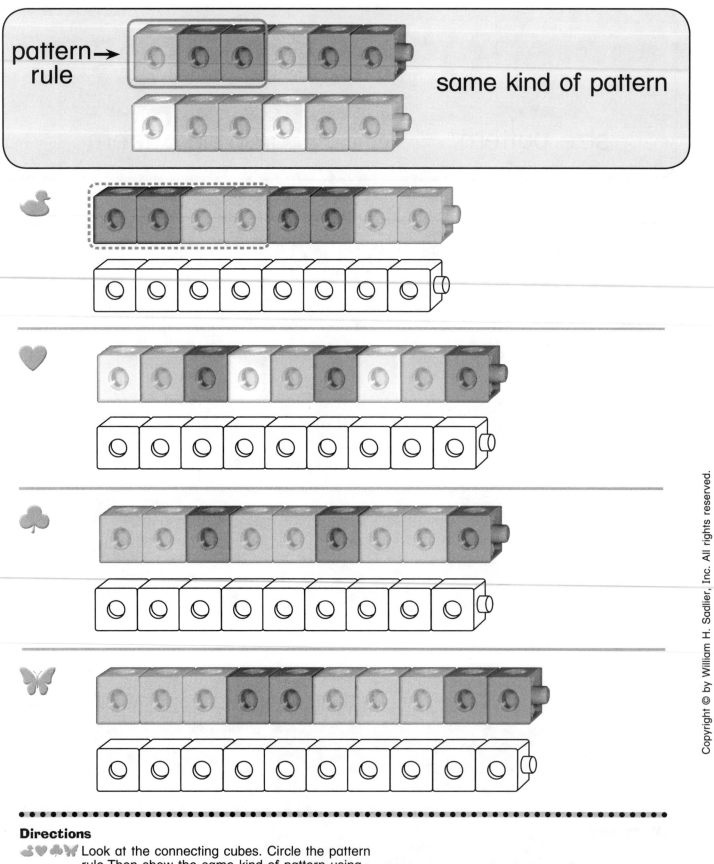

pattern→
rule

same kind of pattern

Directions

Look at the connecting cubes. Circle the pattern
rule. Then show the same kind of pattern using
different colors.

30

Make Patterns

Name _____

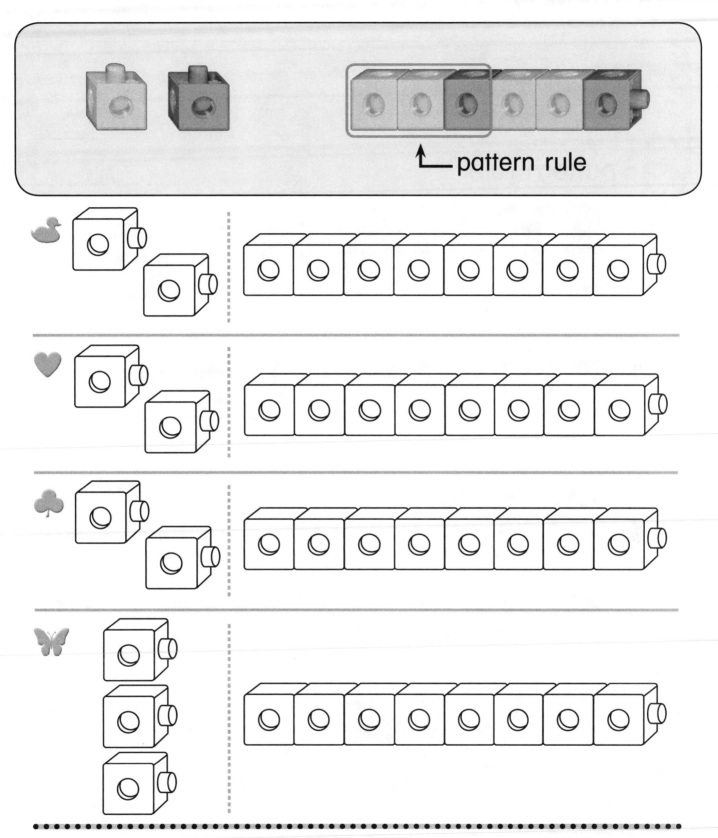

pattern rule

Directions

🦆💜♣️🦋 Using different colors, color the cubes at the beginning of the row. Using those colors, make your own different color pattern. Circle the pattern rule.

Use with Lesson 2-13, pages 63–64 in the Student Book.
Then go to Lesson 2-14, pages 65–66 in the Student Book.

Problem-Solving Strategy:
Find a Pattern

Name _____

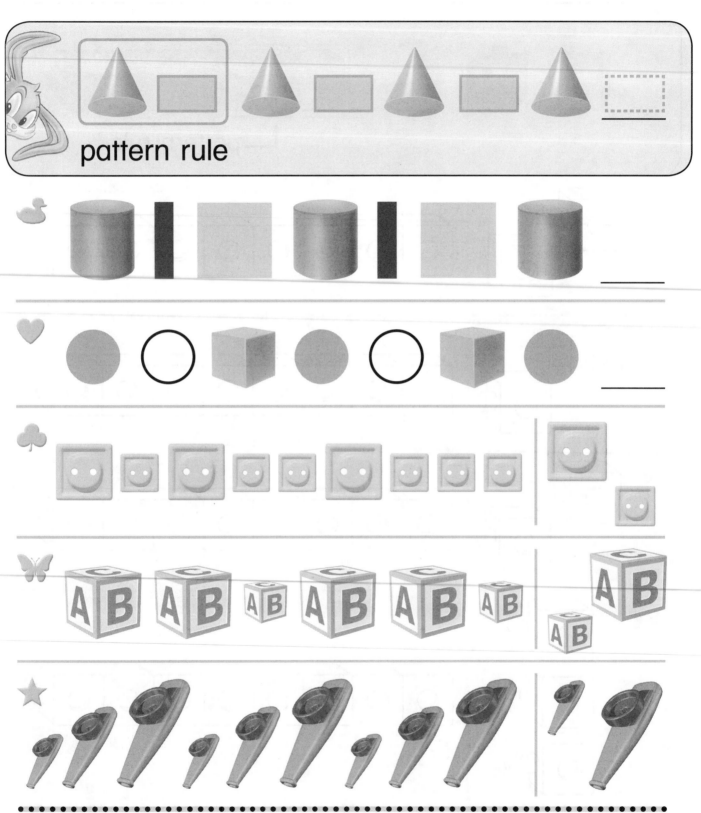

pattern rule

Directions

🦆 💜 Look for a pattern. Circle the pattern rule.
Draw the figure that is most likely to come next.

♣ 🦋 ⭐ Circle the object most likely to come next in the
pattern.

32

Use with Lesson 2-14, pages 65–66 in the Student Book.

Above, Below

Name _____

above

below

Directions

🦆♥♣🦋 Circle the object *above*. Put an ✗ on the object *below*.

....

C Use with Lesson 3-1, pages 77–78 in the Student Book.
C Then go to Lesson 3-2, pages 79–80 in the Student Book.

33

Top, Middle, Bottom

Name _____

top — red
middle — blue
bottom — yellow

Directions

Color the animal at the *top*, red. Color the animal in the *middle*, blue. Color the animal at the *bottom*, yellow.

34

Use with Lesson 3-2, pages 79–80 in the Student Book.
Then go to Lesson 3-3, pages 81–82 in the Student Book.

Over, On, Under

Name _____

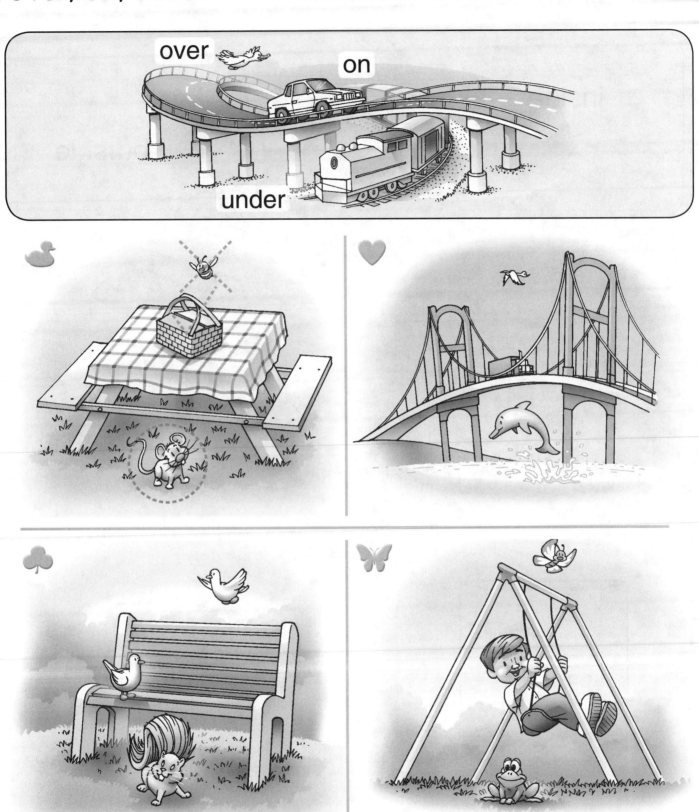

over

on

under

Directions

Put an **X** on what is *over* the object, ✓ what is *on* the object, circle what is *under* the object.

Use with Lesson 3-3, pages 81–82 in the Student Book.

Then go to Lesson 3-4, pages 83–84 in the Student Book.

35

Inside, Outside

Name _____

inside

outside

Directions

🦆❤️♣️🦋 Put an **X** on what is *inside*. Circle what is *outside*.

C Use with Lesson 3-4, pages 83–84 in the Student Book.
C Then go to Lesson 3-4A, pages 149–150 in this Workbook.

In Front, Behind

Name _____

behind

in front

Directions

Circle the animal *in front*. Put an **X** on the animal *behind*.

Use with Lesson 3-5, pages 87–88 in the Student Book.
Then go to Lesson 3-5A, pages 151–152 in this Workbook.

37

Left, Right

Name _____

left   right

···

Directions

Circle the object on the *left*.
Put an ✗ on the object on the *right*.

38

☞ Use with Lesson 3-6, pages 89–90 in the Student Book.
☞ Then go to Lesson 3-7, pages 91–92 in the Student Book.

Left, Between, Right

Name _____

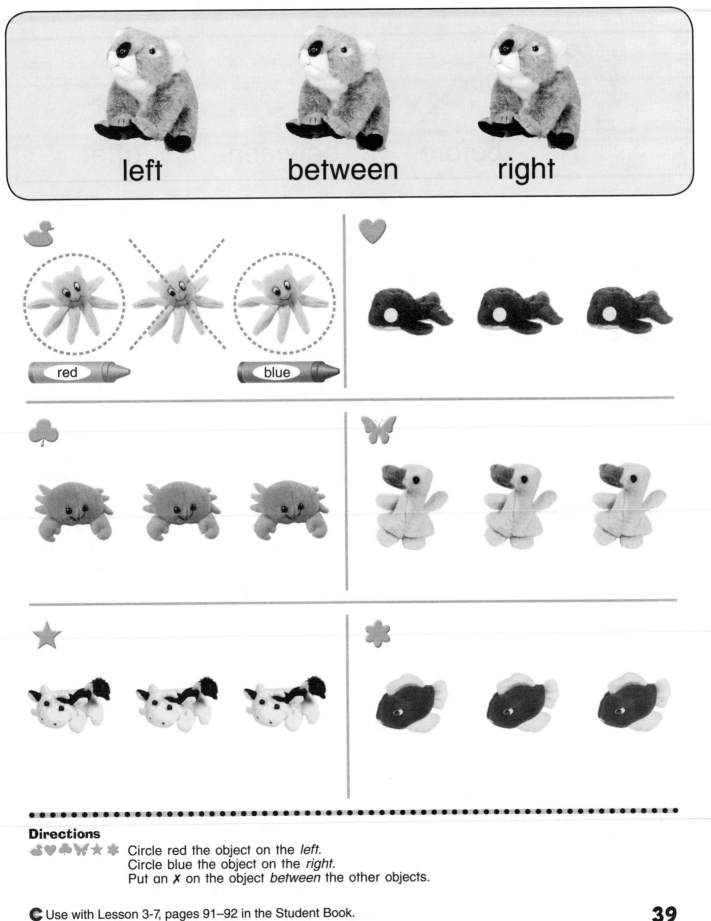

left   between   right

Directions

Circle red the object on the *left*.
Circle blue the object on the *right*.
Put an ✗ on the object *between* the other objects.

C Use with Lesson 3-7, pages 91–92 in the Student Book.
C Then go to Lesson 3-8, pages 93–94 in the Student Book.

39

Before, Between, After

Name _____

before   between   after

Directions

Circle the animal *before* the chick, ✗ the animal after it. ✓ the animal *between* the other animals.

Circle the animal *before* the ostrich, ✗ the animal *after* it. ✓ the animal *between* the other animals.

Circle the animal *before* the peacock, ✗ the animal *after* it. ✓ the animal *between* the other animals.

40   Use with Lesson 3-8, pages 93–94 in the Student Book.
Then go to Lesson 3-9, pages 95–96 in the Student Book.

Problem-Solving Strategy:
Follow Directions/Act It Out

Name _____

Directions

Color blue the bird on the chimney. Color red the flower to the left of the house. ✗ the object above the flower. Circle the pictures over the table. Color orange a picture between the pictures of the bears. Color brown the rug below the table. ✓ the object behind the table.

Use with Lesson 3-9, pages 95–96 in the Student Book.

As Many As

Name _____

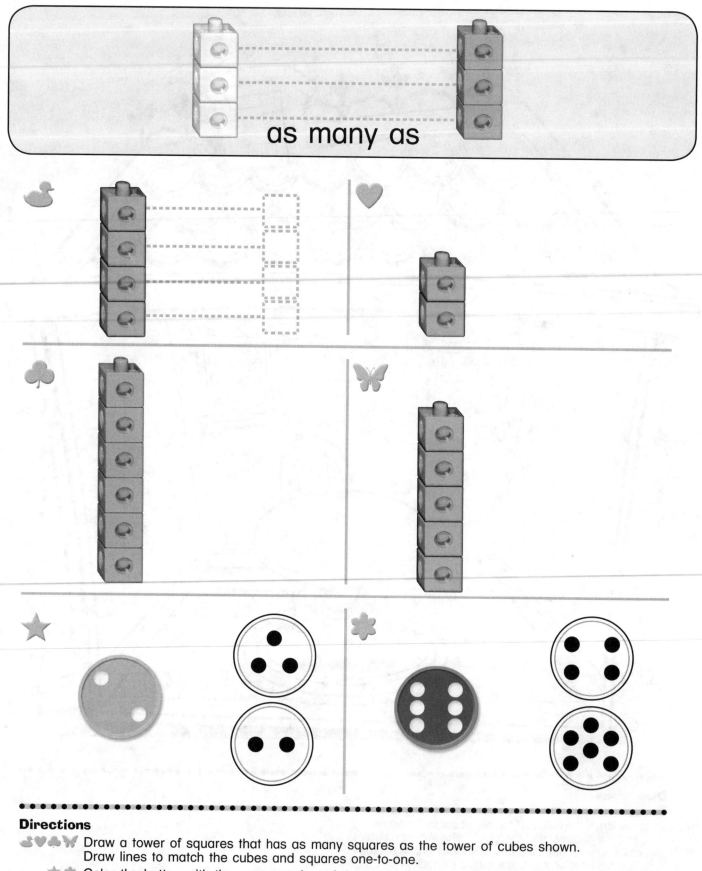

as many as

Directions

Draw a tower of squares that has as many squares as the tower of cubes shown.
Draw lines to match the cubes and squares one-to-one.

Color the button with the same number of dots as the button at the left.

C Use with Lesson 4-1, pages 111–112 in the Student Book.
C Then go to Lesson 4-2, pages 113–114 in the Student Book.

More

Name _____

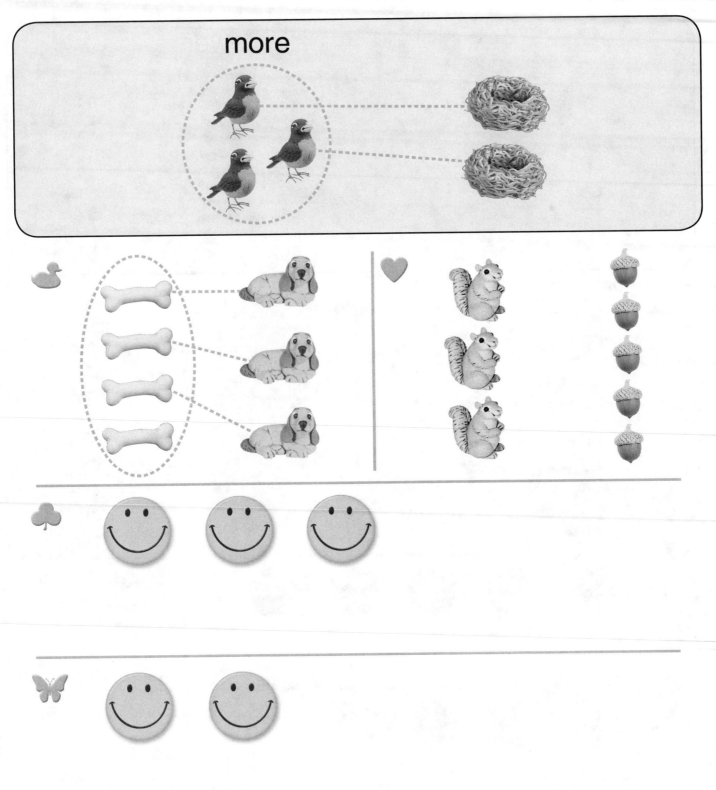

more

Directions

Draw lines to match the objects one-to-one in each group. Circle the group that has more.

Draw a group with more faces than in the group shown.

C Use with Lesson 4-2, pages 113–114 in the Student Book.
C Then go to Lesson 4-3, pages 115–116 in the Student Book.

Fewer

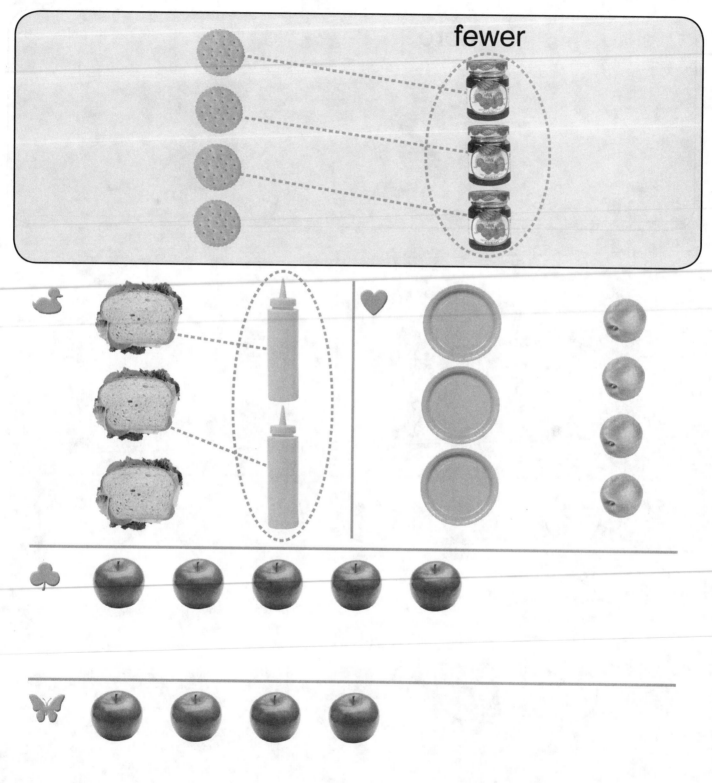

fewer

Directions

Draw lines to match the objects one-to-one in each group. Circle the group that has fewer.

Draw a group with fewer apples than in the group shown.

44

Use with Lesson 4-3, pages 115–116 in the Student Book.
Then go to Lesson 4-4, pages 117–118 in the Student Book.

Fewest, Most

Name _____

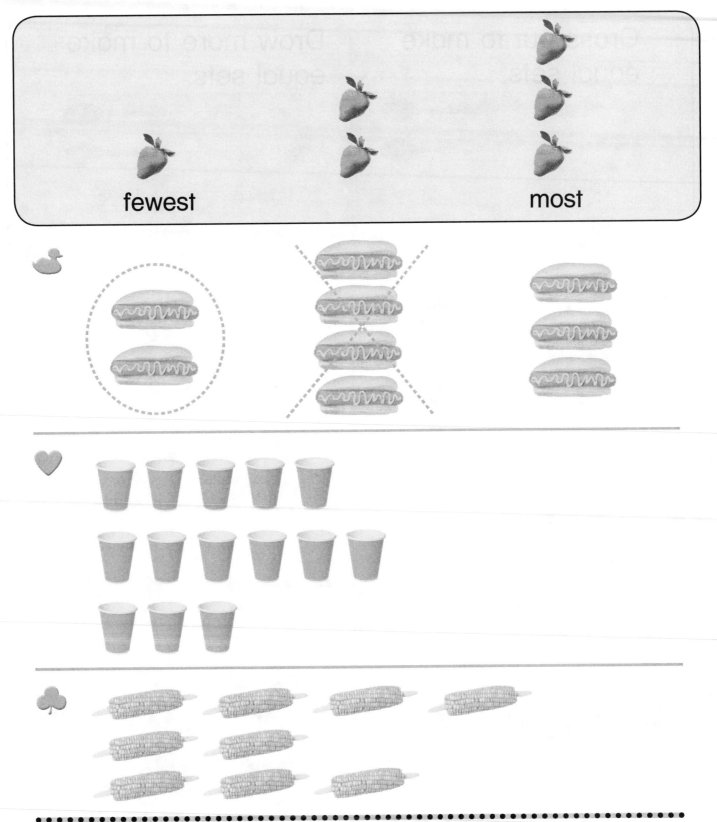

fewest   most

Directions

♣♥♣ Circle the group that has the fewest.
✗ the group that has the most.

....

C Use with Lesson 4-4, pages 117–118 in the Student Book.
Then go to Lesson 4-5, pages 119–120 in the Student Book.

Equalizing Sets

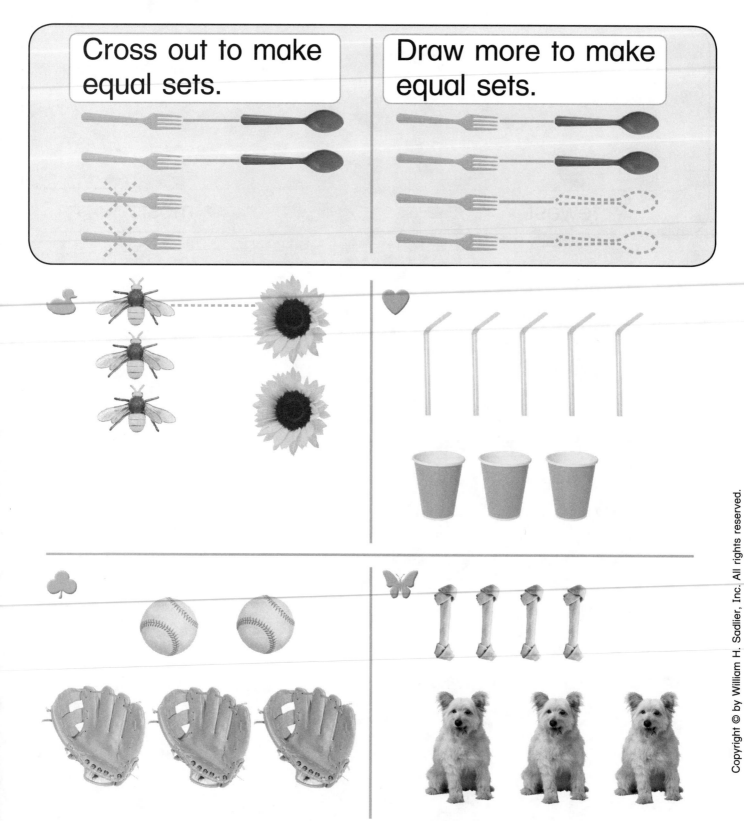

Cross out to make equal sets.

Draw more to make equal sets.

Directions

Make equal sets. Draw more objects or cross out extra objects to make the sets equal.

46

Identify and Write
0 and 1

Name _____

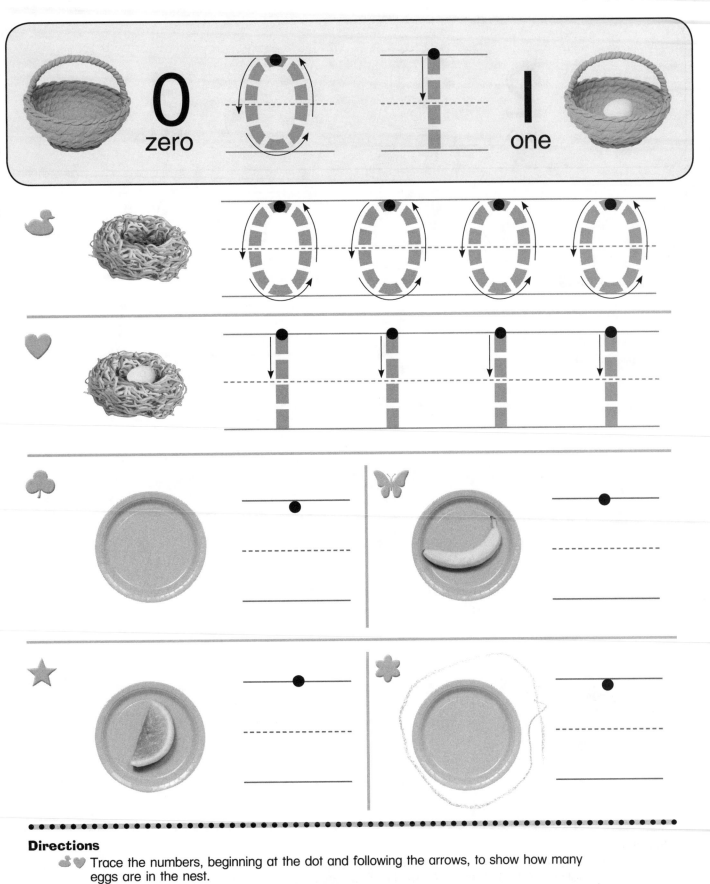

0 zero   one 1

Directions

Trace the numbers, beginning at the dot and following the arrows, to show how many eggs are in the nest.

Write 0 or 1 to show how many objects are on the plate.

C Use with Lesson 4-6, pages 123–124 in the Student Book.
C Then go to Lesson 4-7, pages 125–126 in the Student Book.

Identify and Write
2 and 3

Name _____

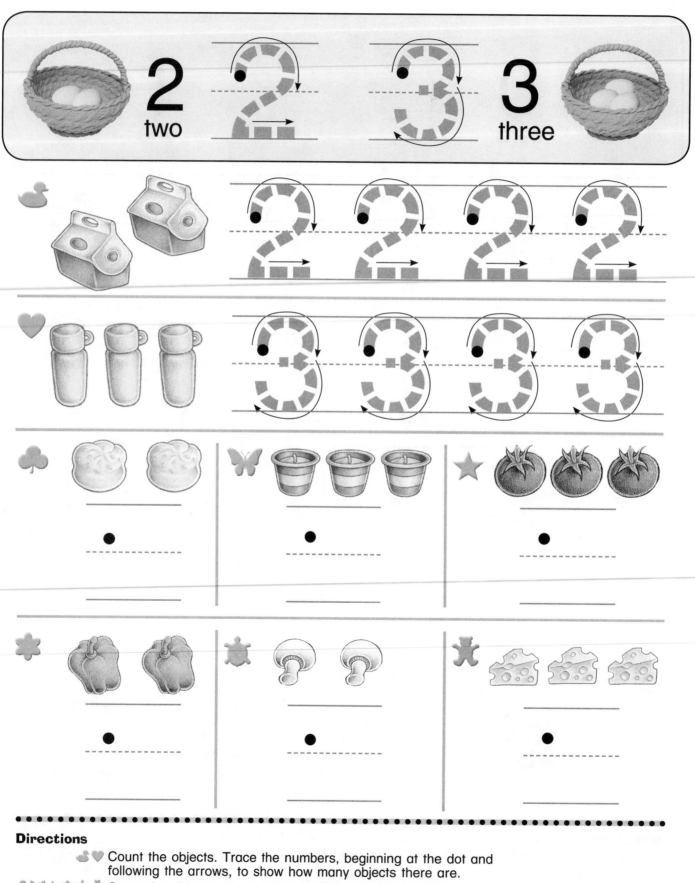

Directions

🦆❤️ Count the objects. Trace the numbers, beginning at the dot and following the arrows, to show how many objects there are.

♣🦋⭐✿🐢🧸 Count the objects. Write the number to show how many.

48

C Use with Lesson 4-7, pages 125–126 in the Student Book.
C Then go to Lesson 4-8, pages 127–128 in the Student Book.

Identify and Write
4 and 5

Name _____

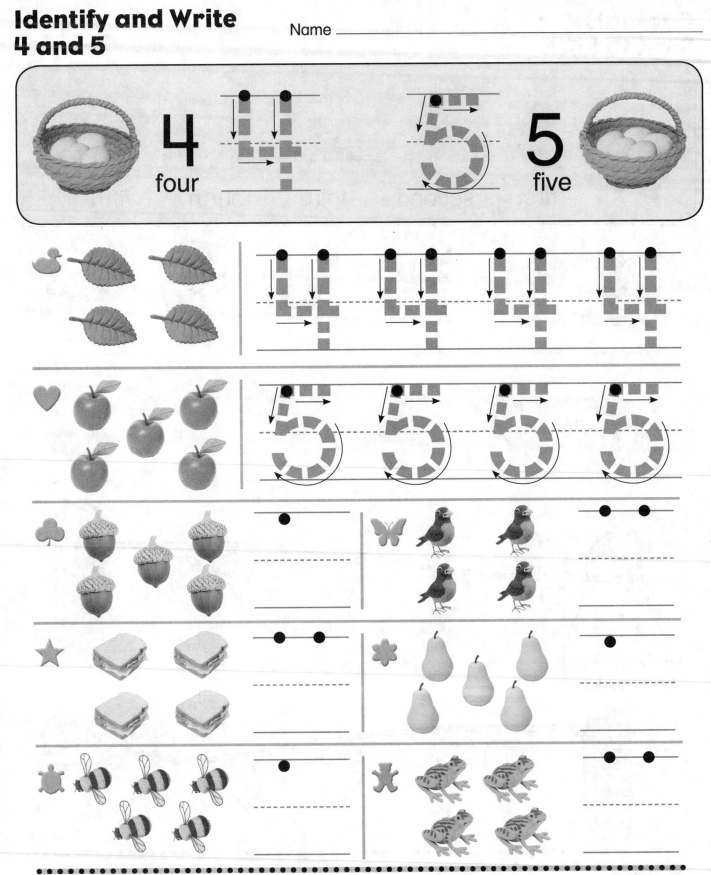

Directions

🦆♥ Count the objects. Trace the numbers, beginning at the dot and following the arrows, to show how many objects there are.

♣🦋✿🐢🐢 Count the objects. Write the number to show how many.

C Use with Lesson 4-8, pages 127–128 in the Student Book.
C Then go to Lessons 4-8A, 4-8B, and 4-8C, pages 153–158 in this Workbook.

Ordinals: First to Fifth

Name _____

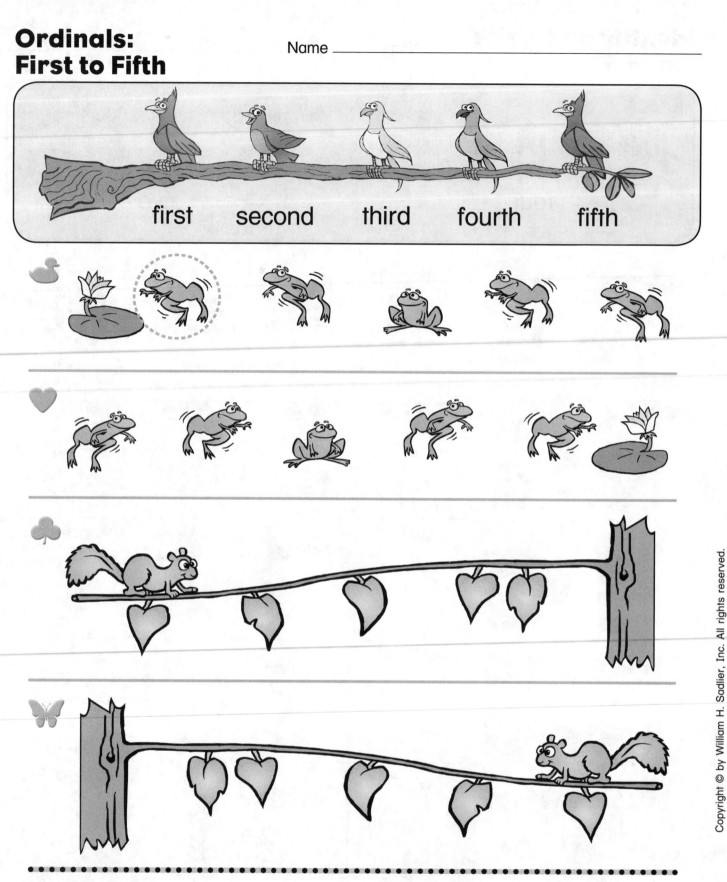

first   second   third   fourth   fifth

Directions

🦆 Circle the frog that is first in line, ✓ the third, and put an ✗ on the fourth frog.

💜 Circle the second frog, ✓ the fourth, and put an ✗ on the fifth frog.

♣ Circle the first leaf, ✓ the third, and put an ✗ on the fourth leaf from the tree.

🦋 Circle the second leaf and ✓ the fifth leaf from the tree.

50

Use with Lesson 4-9, pages 129–130 in the Student Book.
Then go to Lesson 4-10, pages 133–134 in the Student Book.

Identify and Write
6 and 7

Name _____

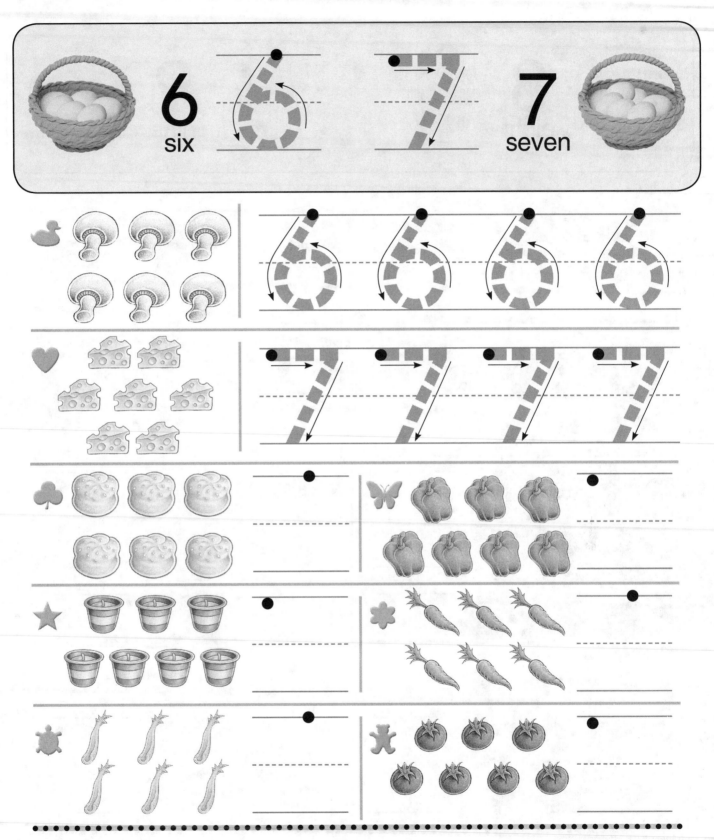

6 six   7 seven

Directions

🦆❤ Count the objects. Trace the numbers, beginning at the dot and following the arrows, to show how many objects there are.

♣🦋★✿✹ Count the objects. Write the number to show how many.

C Use with Lesson 4-10, pages 133–134 in the Student Book.
C Then go to Lesson 4-10A, pages 159–160 in this Workbook.

51

Identify and Write
8 and 9

Name _____

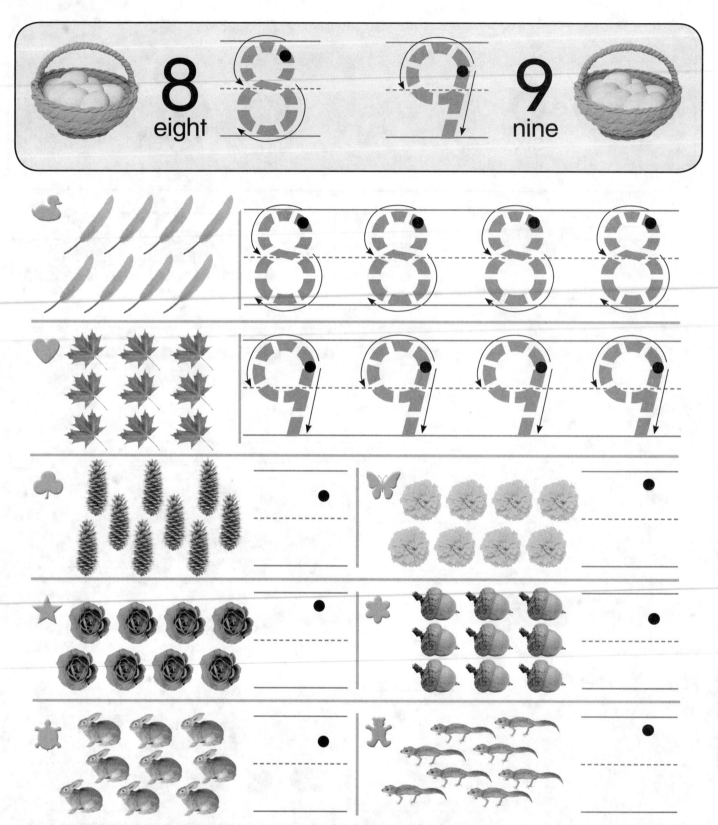

8 eight

9 nine

Directions

🦆💜 Count the objects. Trace the numbers, beginning at the dot and following the arrows, to show how many objects there are.

♣🦋★✿❋ Count the objects. Write the number to show how many.

52

◖ Use with Lesson 4-11, pages 135–136 in the Student Book.
◖ Then go to Lesson 4-11A, pages 161–162 in this Workbook.

Identify and Write 10

Name _____

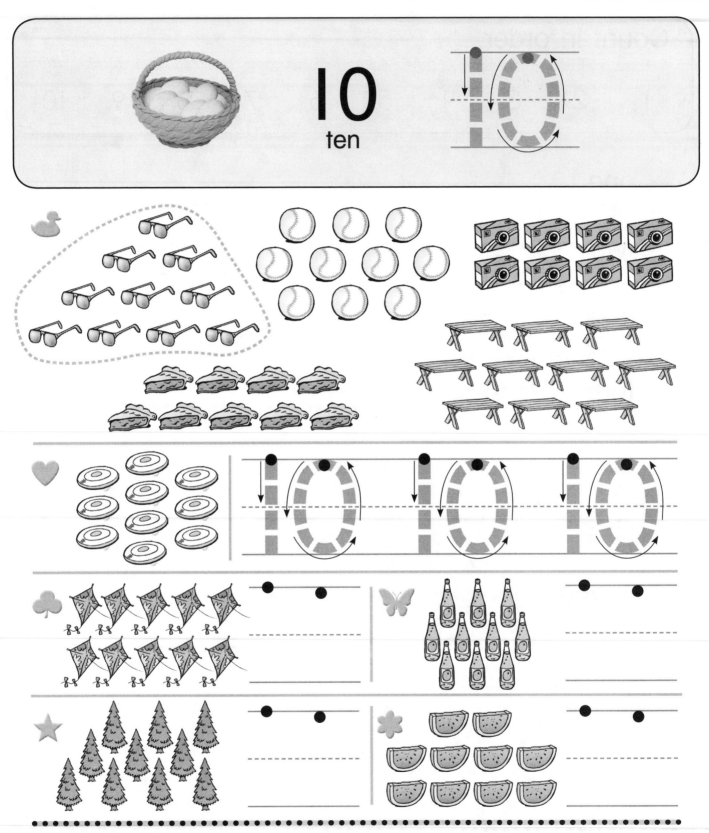

10
ten

Directions

🦆 Circle the groups of 10.

💜 Trace the numbers, beginning at the dot and following the arrows, to show how many objects there are.

♣🦋⭐✳ Count the objects. Write the number to show how many.

C Use with Lesson 4-12, pages 137–138 in the Student Book.

C Then go to Lessons 4-12A, 4-12B, and 4-12C, pages 163–168 in this Workbook.

53

Numbers 1–10

Name _____

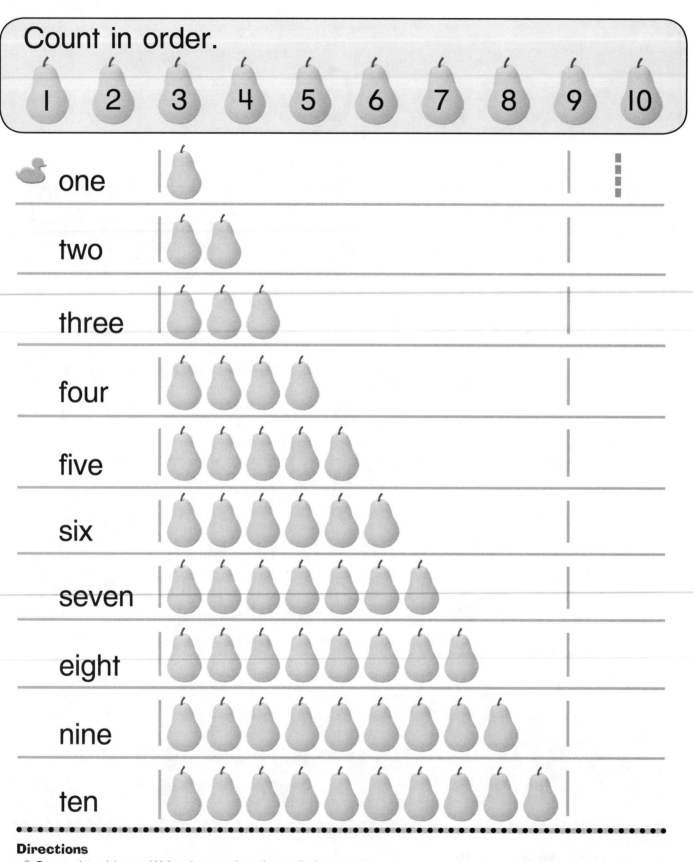

Count in order.

1 2 3 4 5 6 7 8 9 10

🦆 one

two

three

four

five

six

seven

eight

nine

ten

Directions

🦆 Count the objects. Write the number that tells how many.

C Use with Lesson 4-13, pages 139–140 in the Student Book.
C Then go to Lesson 4-14, pages 141–142 in the Student Book.

Number Line

Name _____

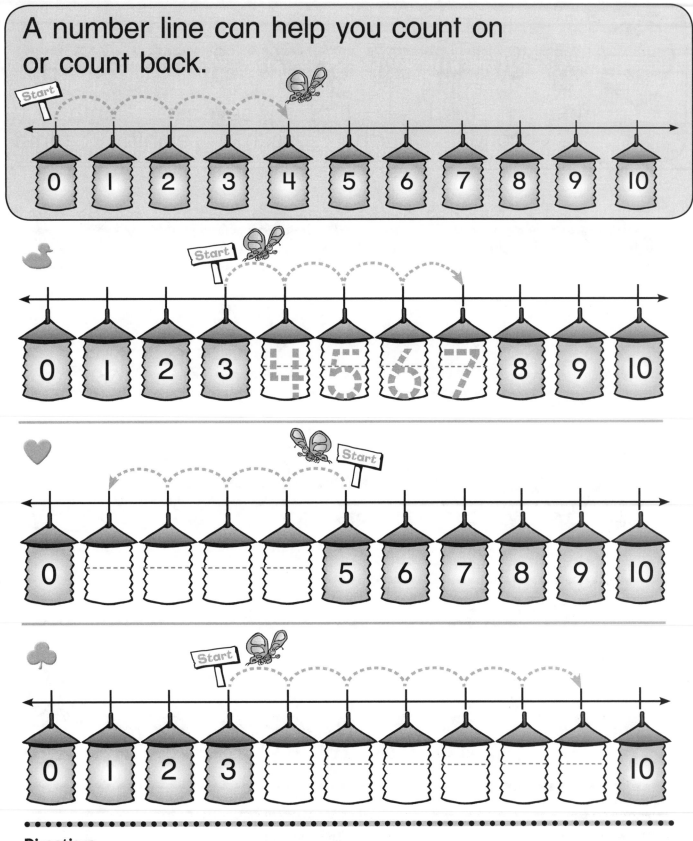

A number line can help you count on or count back.

Start

0 1 2 3 4 5 6 7 8 9 10

Start

0 1 2 3 **4 5 6 7** 8 9 10

Start

0 ___ ___ ___ 5 6 7 8 9 10

Start

0 1 2 3 ___ ___ ___ ___ ___ 10

Directions

Follow the butterfly and count on or back to fill in the missing numbers. Write the missing numbers.

Use with Lesson 4-14, pages 141–142 in the Student Book.
Then go to Lesson 4-14A, pages 169–170 in this Workbook.

55

Ordinals: First to Tenth

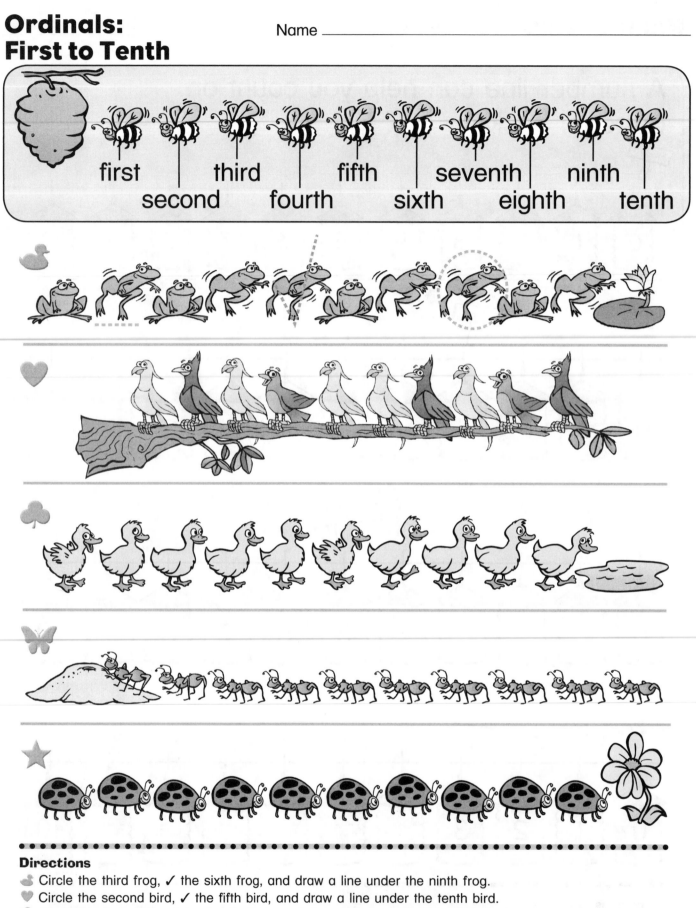

first
second
third
fourth
fifth
sixth
seventh
eighth
ninth
tenth

Directions

🦆 Circle the third frog, ✓ the sixth frog, and draw a line under the ninth frog.

❤ Circle the second bird, ✓ the fifth bird, and draw a line under the tenth bird.

♣ Circle the first duck, ✓ the fourth duck, and draw a line under the eighth duck.

🦋 Circle the third ant, ✓ the seventh ant, and draw a line under the tenth ant.

★ Circle the sixth ladybug, ✓ the eighth ladybug, and draw a line under the ninth ladybug.

56

Use with Lesson 4-15, pages 143–144 in the Student Book.
Then go to Lesson 4-16, pages 145–146 in the Student Book.

Number Patterns

Name _____

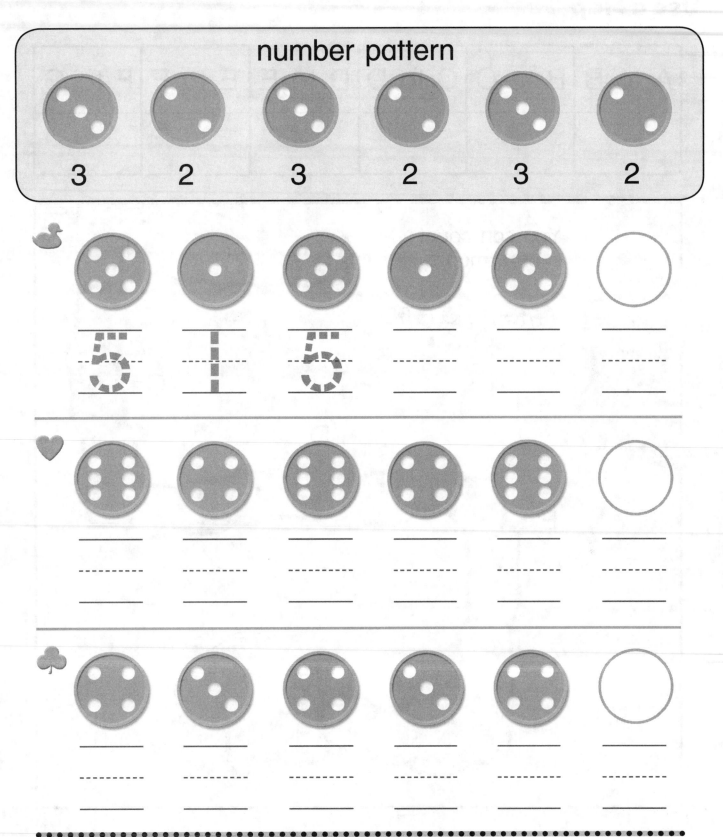

number pattern

| 3 | 2 | 3 | 2 | 3 | 2 |

🦆 5 1 5 ___ ___ ___

♥ ___ ___ ___ ___ ___ ___

♣ ___ ___ ___ ___ ___ ___

Directions
🦆♥♣ Look for a pattern. Count the dots. Write the number below.
Then draw and write what is most likely to come next in the
number pattern.

Use with Lesson 4-16, pages 145–146 in the Student Book.
♣ Then go to Lesson 4-17, pages 147–148 in the Student Book.

57

Problem-Solving Strategy:
Use a Map

Name _____

A to B	B to C	C to D	D to E	E to F	F to G
5					

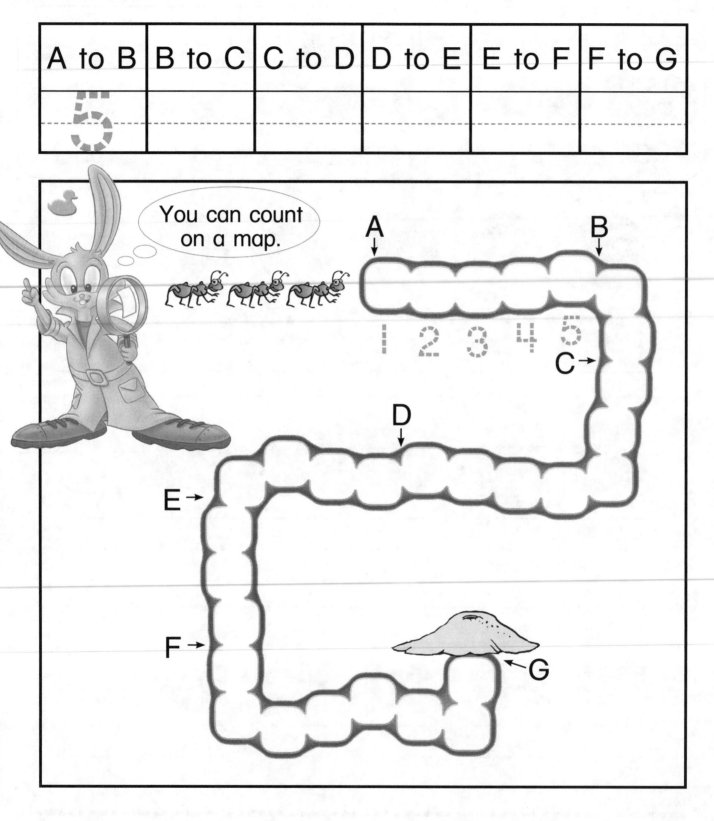

You can count on a map.

Directions

How many boxes are there from A to B? B to C? C to D? D to E? E to F? F to G?
Write the numbers. Color the squares on each part of the path a different color.

Use with Lesson 4-17, pages 147–148 in the Student Book.

Identify and Write
11 and 12

Name _____

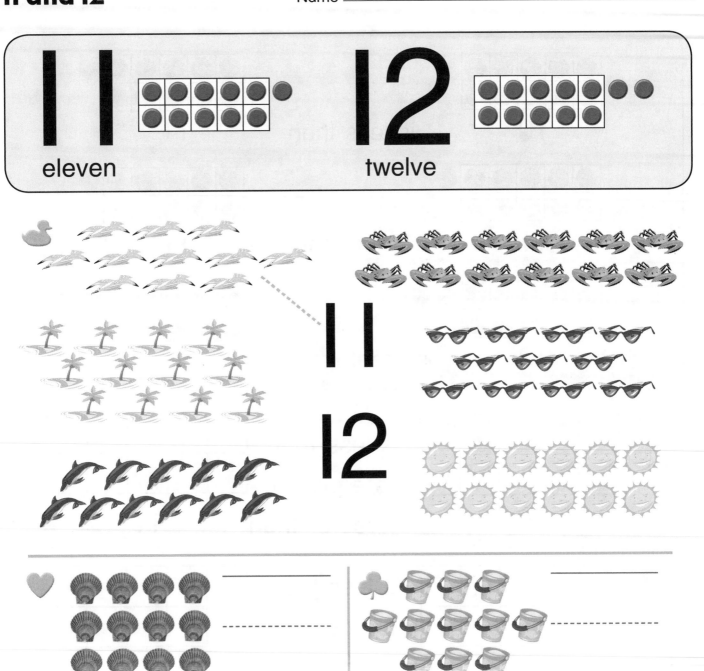

Directions

Count the number of objects in each group.
Draw a line to match each group with the correct number of items in that group.

♥♣🦋★ Count the objects. Then write how many.

C Use with Lesson 5-1, pages 159–160 in the Student Book.
C Then go to Lesson 5-2, pages 161–162 in the Student Book.

Compare Numbers to 12   Name _____

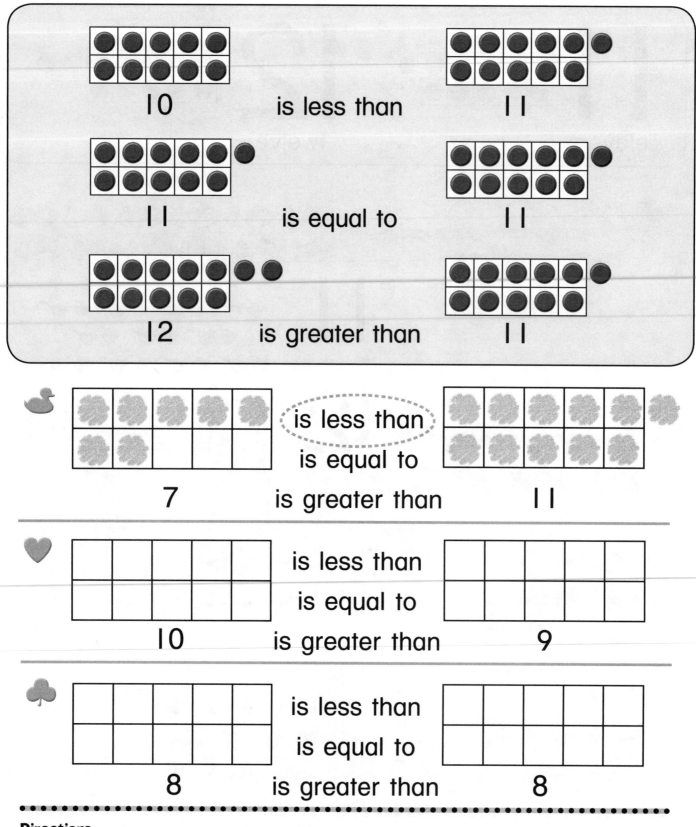

10   is less than   11

11   is equal to   11

12   is greater than   11

🦆   is less than
    ⟨is less than⟩
    is equal to
7   is greater than   11

❤   is less than
    is equal to
10   is greater than   9

♣   is less than
    is equal to
8   is greater than   8

Directions
🦆 ❤ ♣ Draw dots to show the numbers in each row. Circle to show whether the number on the left *is less than*, *is equal to*, or *is greater than* the number at the right.

C Use with Lesson 5-2, pages 161–162 in the Student Book.
C Then go to Lesson 5-3, pages 163–164 in the Student Book.

Order Numbers to 12 Name _____

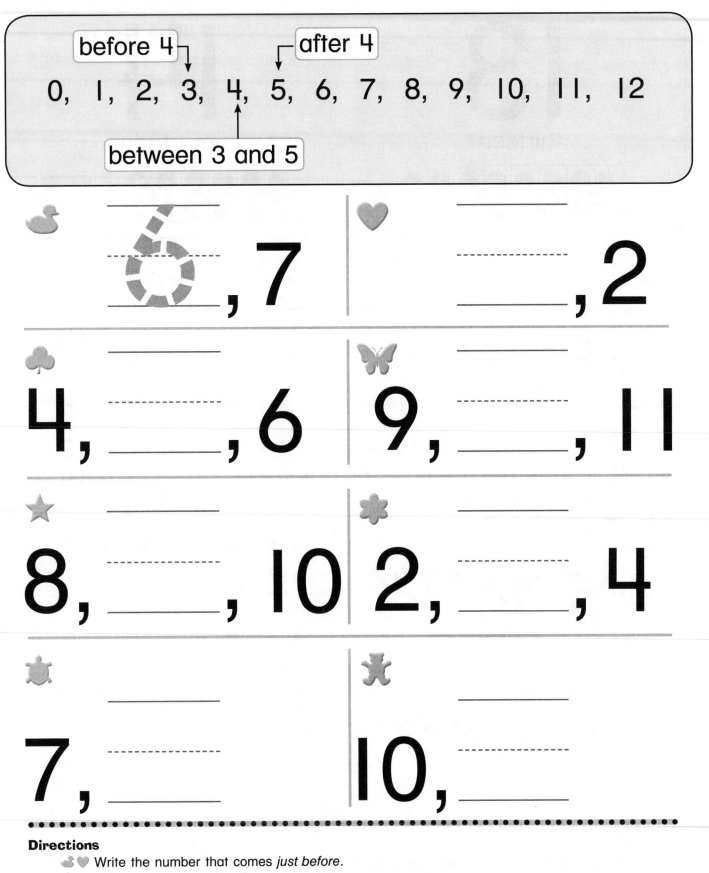

before 4 →

after 4

0, 1, 2, 3, 4, 5, 6, 7, 8, 9, 10, 11, 12

between 3 and 5

6 , 7   ____ , 2

4, ____ , 6   9, ____ , 11

8, ____ , 10   2, ____ , 4

7, ____   10, ____

Directions

Write the number that comes *just before*.

Write the number that comes *between*.

Write the number that comes *just after*.

C Use with Lesson 5-3, pages 163–164 in the Student Book.
C Then go to Lesson 5-4, pages 165–166 in the Student Book.

61

Identify and Write
13 and 14

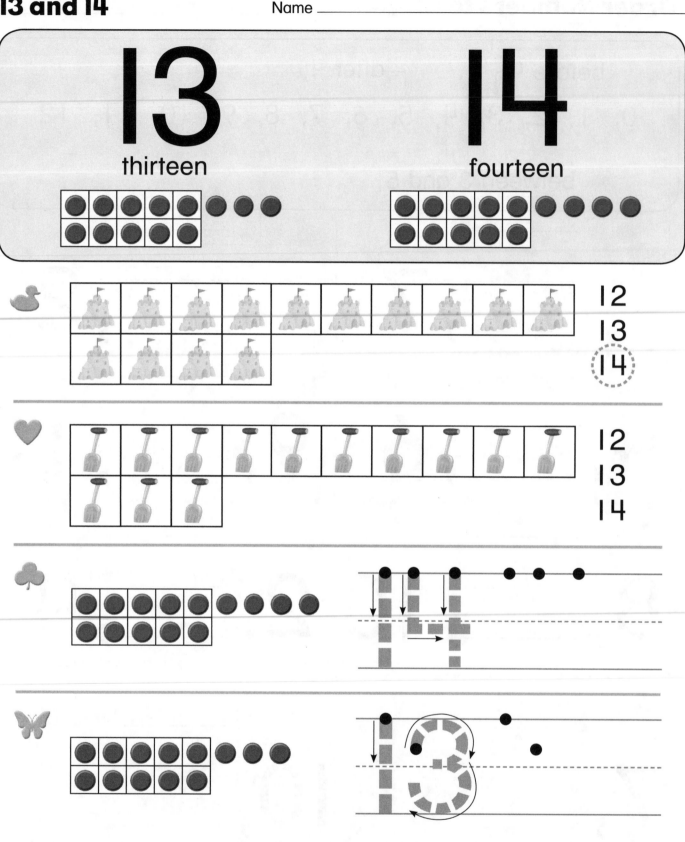

13 thirteen

14 fourteen

🦆 | 12
13
⑭

❤️ | 12
13
14

♣️

🦋

Directions

🦆❤️ Circle the number that shows how many objects there are.

♣️🦋 Count, then show how many by tracing and writing the number.
Begin at the dot and follow the arrows.

C Use with Lesson 5-4, pages 165–166 in the Student Book.
C Then go to Lesson 5-5, pages 167–168 in the Student Book.

Identify and Write
15 and 16

Name _____

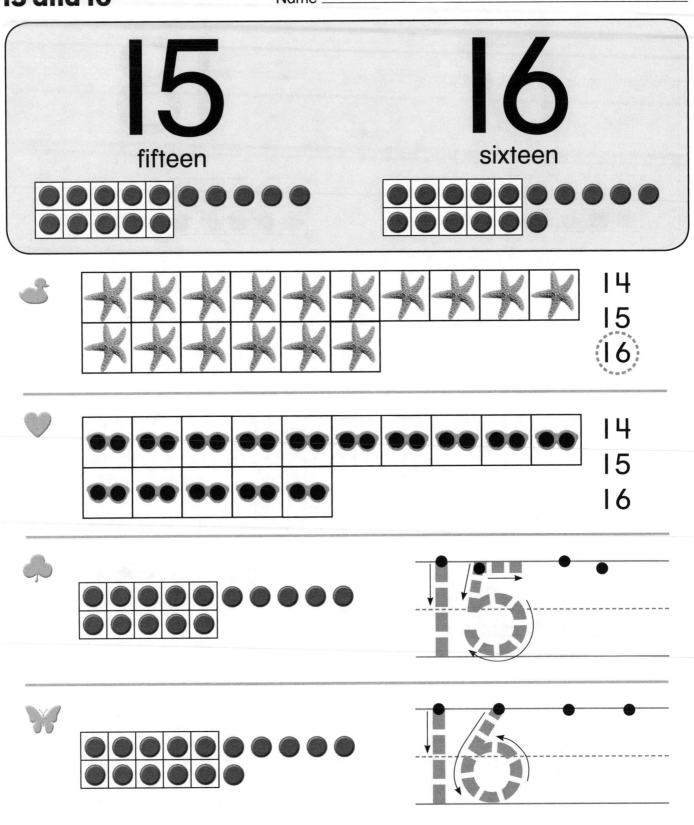

15 fifteen

16 sixteen

🦆   14   15   ⟨16⟩

♥   14   15   16

Directions

🦆♥ Circle the number that shows how many objects there are.

♣🦋 Count, then show how many by tracing and writing the number. Begin at the dot and follow the arrows.

C Use with Lesson 5-5, pages 167–168 in the Student Book.
C Then go to Lesson 5-6, pages 169–170 in the Student Book.

63

Identify and Write
17 and 18

Name _____

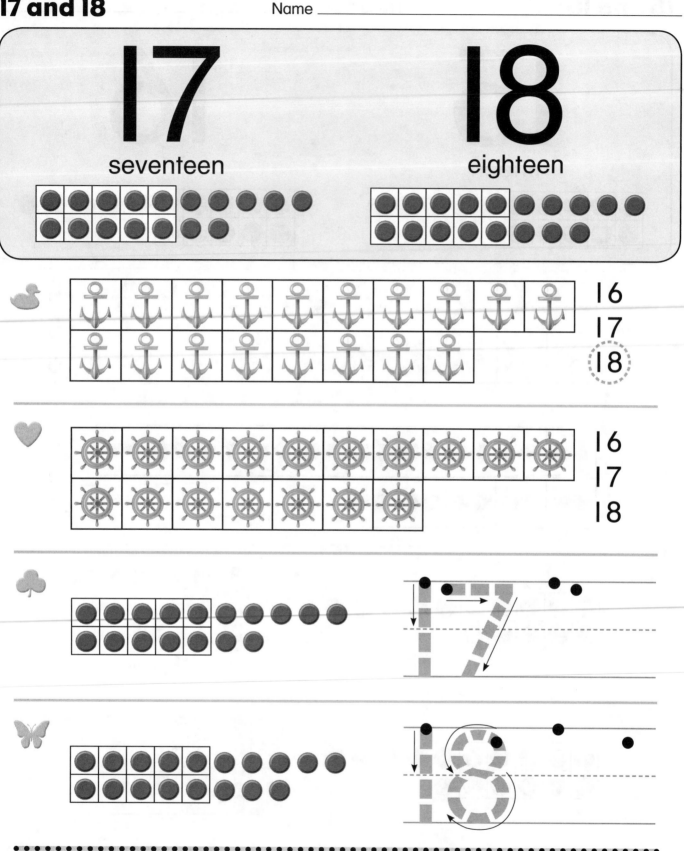

17 seventeen

18 eighteen

16
17
18

16
17
18

Directions

🦆♥ Circle the number that shows how many objects there are.

♣🦋 Count, then show how many by tracing and writing the number.
Begin at the dot and follow the arrows.

C Use with Lesson 5-6, pages 169–170 in the Student Book.
C Then go to Lesson 5-7, pages 171–172 in the Student Book.

Identify and Write
19 and 20

Name _____

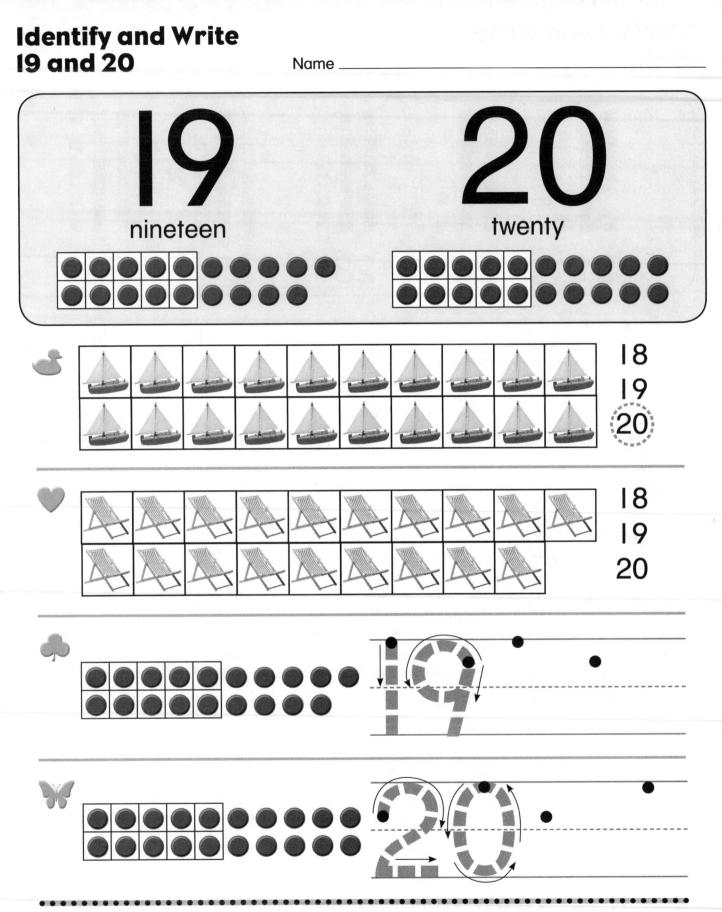

Directions

🦆💜 Circle the number that shows how many objects there are.

♣🦋 Count, then show how many by tracing and writing the number. Begin at the dot and follow the arrows.

C Use with Lesson 5-7, pages 171–172 in the Student Book.
C Then go to Lessons 5-7A and 5-7B, pages 171–174 in this Workbook.

65

Identify and Write
21–25

Name _____

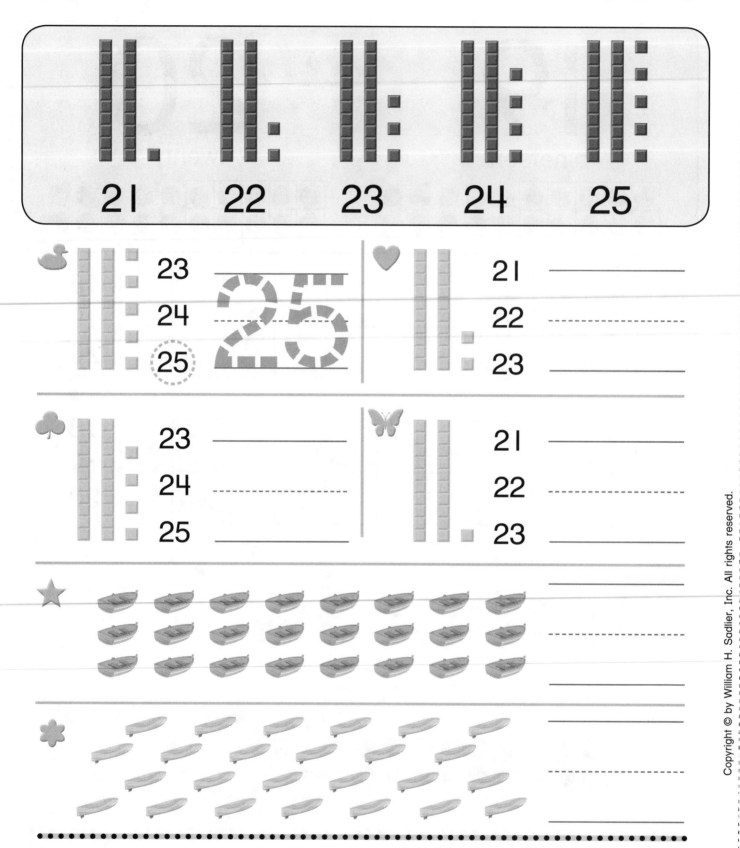

21   22   23   24   25

🦆 23 [25] 25
    24
    ⟨25⟩

♥ 21 _____
   22 _____
   23 _____

♣ 23 _____
   24 _____
   25 _____

🦋 21 _____
    22 _____
    23 _____

⭐ _____

✿ _____

Directions

🦆♥♣🦋 Circle the number that shows how many. Then write the number.

⭐✿ Circle groups of 10. Count on any extras. Write the number.

66

C Use with Lesson 5-8, pages 175–176 in the Student Book.
C Then go to Lesson 5-9, pages 177–178 in the Student Book.

Identify and Write
26–31

Name _____

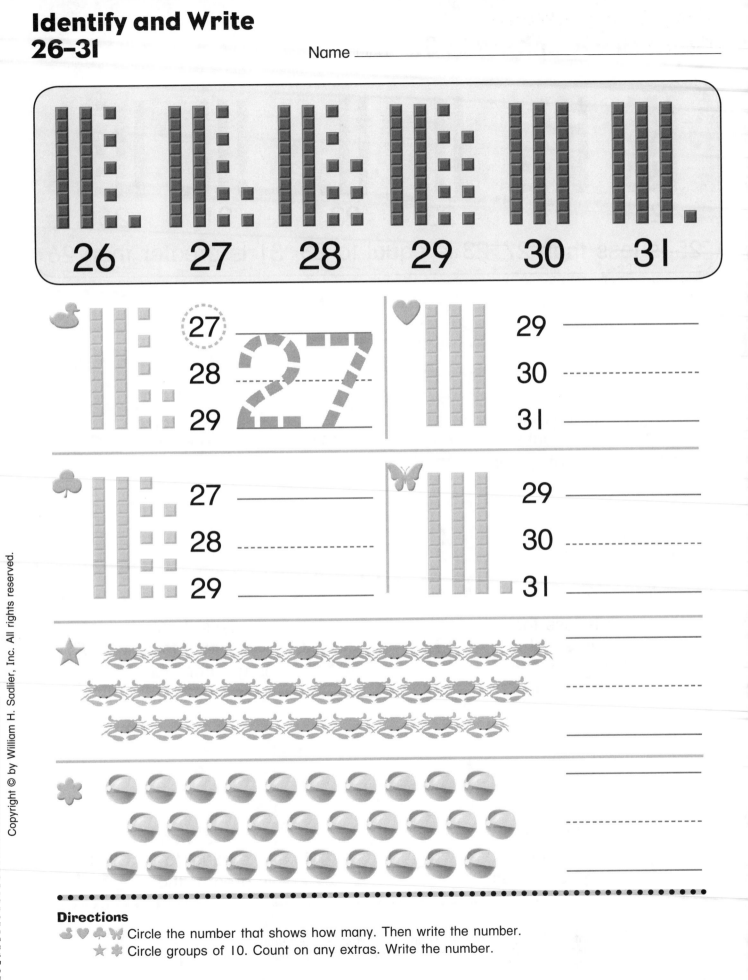

26   27   28   29   30   31

27 (circled)   _____
28   - - - - - - - -
29   _____

29   _____
30   - - - - - - - -
31   _____

27   _____
28   - - - - - - - -
29   _____

29   _____
30   - - - - - - - -
31   _____

_____

- - - - - - - - - -

_____

_____

- - - - - - - - - -

_____

Directions
Circle the number that shows how many. Then write the number.

Circle groups of 10. Count on any extras. Write the number.

Use with Lesson 5-9, pages 177–178 in the Student Book.
Then go to Lesson 5-10, pages 179–180 in the Student Book.

Compare Numbers to 31

Name _____

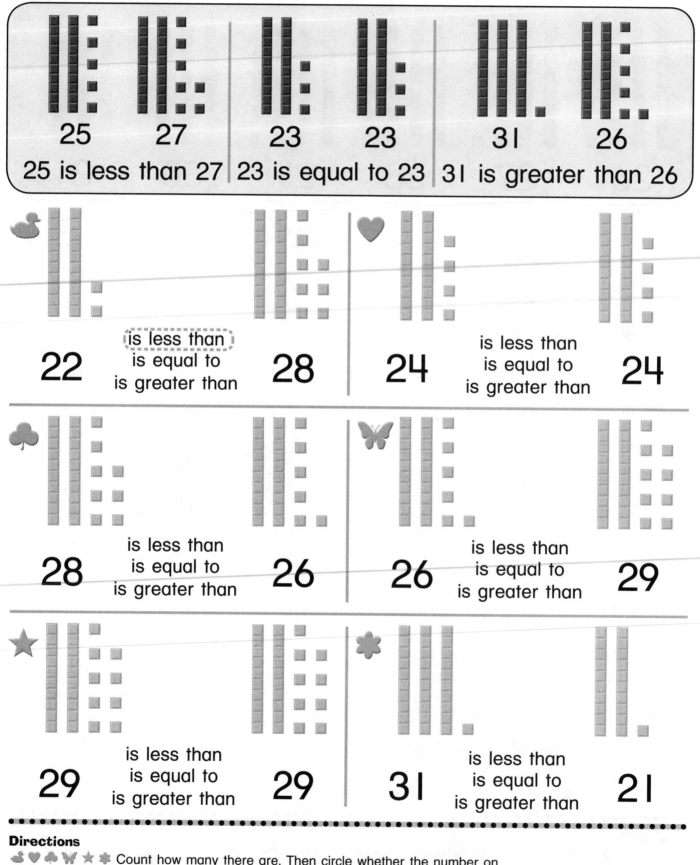

25 **27**	**23** **23**	**31** **26**
25 is less than 27	23 is equal to 23	31 is greater than 26

🦆 **22**   (is less than) / is equal to / is greater than   **28**

❤️ **24**   is less than / is equal to / is greater than   **24**

♣️ **28**   is less than / is equal to / is greater than   **26**

🦋 **26**   is less than / is equal to / is greater than   **29**

⭐ **29**   is less than / is equal to / is greater than   **29**

❀ **31**   is less than / is equal to / is greater than   **21**

Directions

🦆 ❤️ ♣️ 🦋 ⭐ ❀ Count how many there are. Then circle whether the number on the left *is less than*, *is equal to*, or *is greater than* the number on the right.

Use with Lesson 5-10, pages 179–180 in the Student Book.
C Then go to Lesson 5-11, pages 181–182 in the Student Book.

Order Numbers to 31 Name _____

before 27

21, 22, 23, 24, 25, 26, 27, 28, 29, 30, 31

after 27

between 26 and 28

27, 28

___, 31

29, ___

23, ___

19, ___, 21

24, ___, 26

17   18   ___   20

Directions
Write the number that comes just before.
Write the number that comes just after.
Write the number that comes between.
Write the missing numbers on the number line so the numbers are in counting order.

Use with Lesson 5-11, pages 181–182 in the Student Book.
Then go to Lesson 5-12, pages 183–184 in the Student Book.

69

Estimate Groups

Name _____

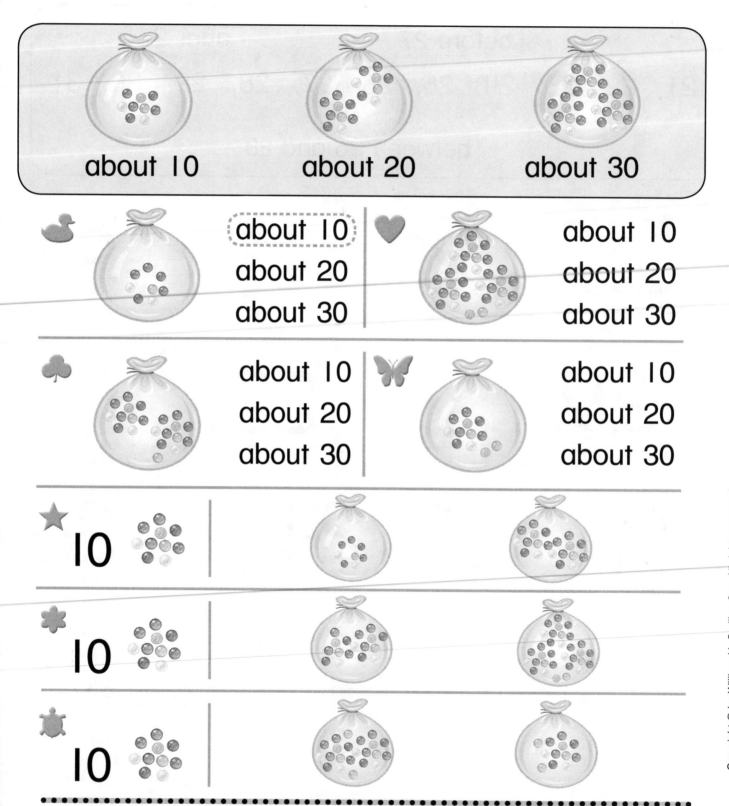

about 10   about 20   about 30

🦆   (about 10)   ❤   about 10
     about 20   about 20
     about 30   about 30

♣   about 10   🦋   about 10
     about 20   about 20
     about 30   about 30

⭐ 10

✿ 10

🐢 10

Directions

🦆❤♣🦋 Estimate the number of marbles. Circle *about 10*, *about 20*, or *about 30* to show which number is the best estimate. Count the number of marbles to check.

⭐ Estimate. Circle the bag that has about 10 marbles.

✿ Estimate. Circle the bag that has about 30 marbles.

🐢 Estimate. Circle the bag that has about 20 marbles.

70

Use with Lesson 5-12, pages 183–184 in the Student Book.
Then go to Lesson 5-13, pages 185–186 in the Student Book.

Problem-Solving Strategy: Guess and Test

Name _____

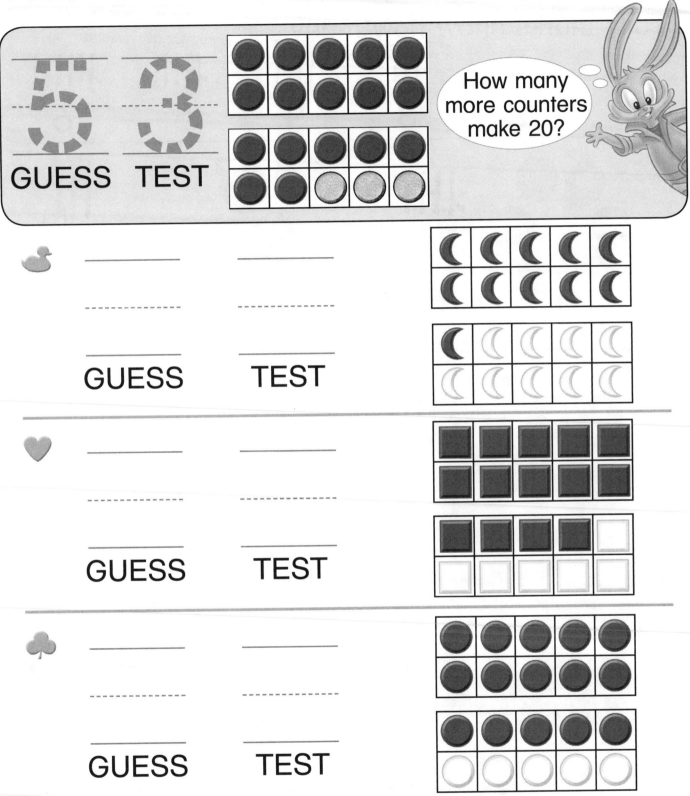

GUESS   TEST

How many more counters make 20?

🦆 _____ _____

    - - - - -   - - - - -

    _____   _____

    GUESS   TEST

♥ _____ _____

    - - - - -   - - - - -

    _____   _____

    GUESS   TEST

♣ _____ _____

    - - - - -   - - - - -

    _____   _____

    GUESS   TEST

Directions
🦆 There are 11 black moons. How many more moons make 20? Guess. Then color to test.
♥ There are 14 black tiles. How many more tiles make 20? Guess. Then color to test.
♣ There are 15 black counters. How many more counters make 20? Guess. Then color to test.

Use with Lesson 5-13, pages 185–186 in the Student Book.

71

Tally Marks

Tally marks show how many.

$|$	$||$	$|||$	$||||$	$\cancel{||||}$	$\cancel{||||}\,|$
1	2	3	4	5	6

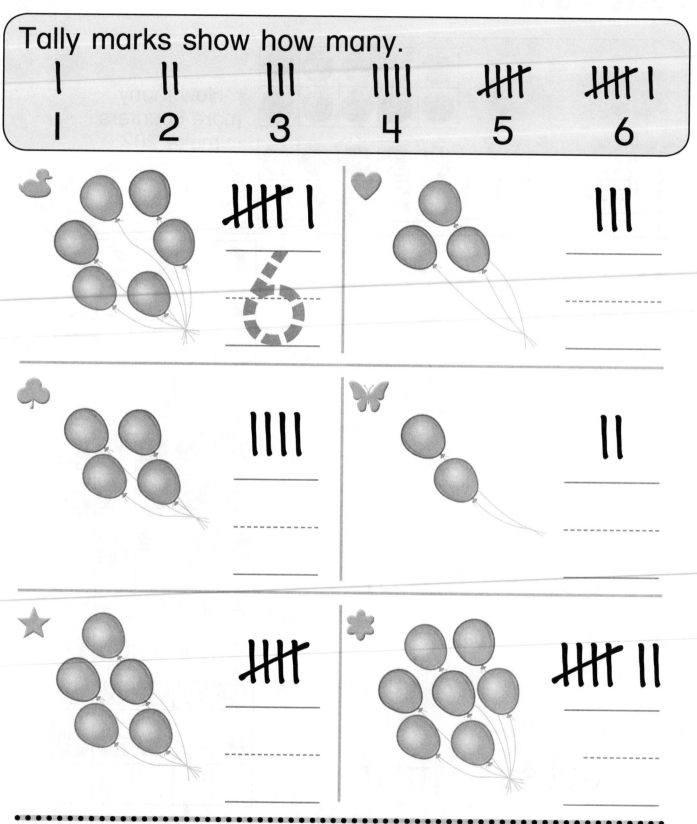

$\cancel{||||}\,|$

6

$|||$

$||||$

$||$

$\cancel{||||}$

$\cancel{||||}\,||$

Directions

Look at the balloons. Then look at the tally marks.
Write how many.

C Use with Lesson 6-1, pages 201–202 in the Student Book.
C Then go to Lesson 6-2, pages 203–204 in the Student Book.

Tally Charts

A tally chart shows
how many of each.

Circus Toys			
Toy	 🥁	 🔮	 🎉
Tally	IIII	IIII IIII	IIII IIII I

Farm Animals at the Fair			
Animal	 🐴	 🐓	 🐖
Tally			

Prizes at the Fair			
Prize	 🚗	 🧸	 🐴
Tally			

Directions

🐥 Tally to show how many of each kind of farm animal.

💜 Tally to show how many of each kind of prize.

© Use with Lesson 6-2, pages 203–204 in the Student Book.
© Then go to Lesson 6-2A, pages 175–176 in this Workbook.

73

Picture Graphs

Name _____

Space Travel Needs

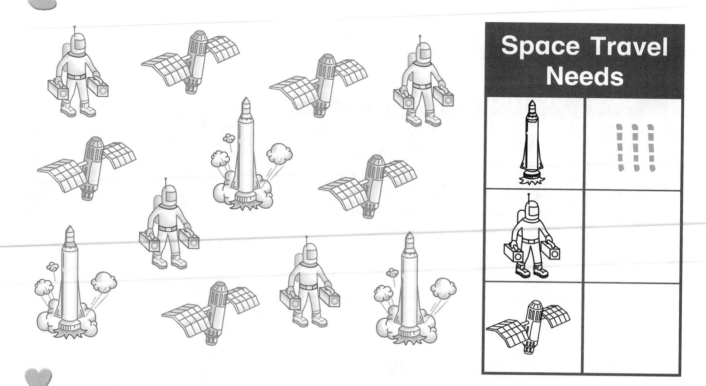

Space Travel Needs	
🚀	∣∣∣ ∣∣∣
👨‍🚀	
🛰️	

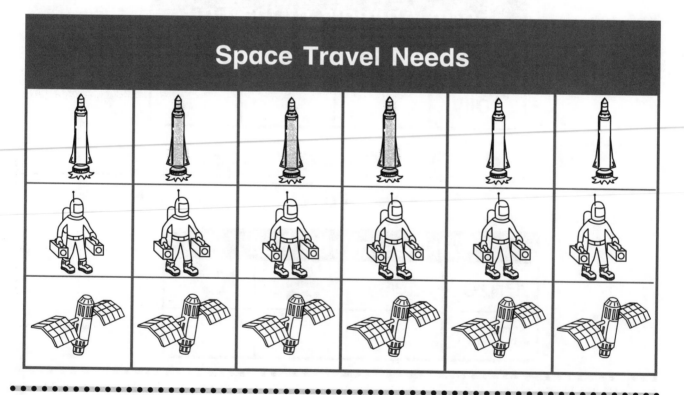

• •

Directions

🦆 Look at the pictures. Complete the tally chart to show how many of each.

💜 Use the tally chart to make a picture graph.
Color one picture for each tally mark.

74

Ⅽ Use with Lesson 6-3, pages 205–206 in the Student Book.
Ⅽ Then go to Lesson 6-4, pages 207–208 in the Student Book.

Pictographs

Name _____

Clowns at the Fair

Clowns at the Fair	
(clown)	卌 卌 ||||
(clown)	
(clown)	

Clowns at the Fair								
(clown)	☺							
(clown)								
(clown)								

Directions

🦆 Look at the clowns. Complete the tally chart to show how many of each type of clown.

♥ Use the tally chart to make a pictograph. Draw one ☺ for each tally mark.

© Use with Lesson 6-4, pages 207–208 in the Student Book.
Then go to Lesson 6-5, pages 209–210 in the Student Book.

75

Surveys and Real Graphs

Name _____

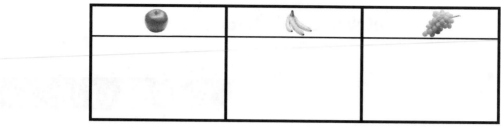

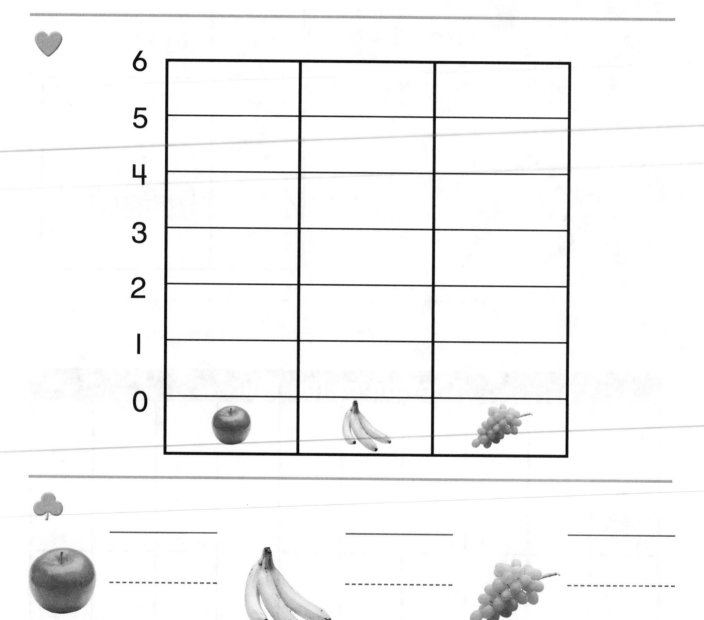

• •

Directions

Survey six friends about their favorite fruit. Tally the results.

Use pennies or paper clips to make a real graph to show your survey results.
Use one object for each tally mark.

Write how many of your friends like each kind of fruit.

76

Bar Graphs

Bugs in the Forest

Bug	Tally
(ant)	~~IIII~~
(ladybug)	
(butterfly)	

Bugs in the Forest

	0	1	2	3	4	5
(ant)						
(ladybug)						
(butterfly)						

(ant) _____ - - - - - - - - -

(ladybug) _____ - - - - - - - - -

(butterfly) _____ - - - - - - - - -

Directions

🦆 Complete the tally chart. Use the tally chart to make a bar graph. Color one ☐ for each tally mark.

💜 Use the bar graph to tell how many of each bug. Write the number.

Use with Lesson 6-6, pages 211–212 in the Student Book.
Then go to Lesson 6-7, pages 215–216 in the Student Book.

Equal Parts

Name _____

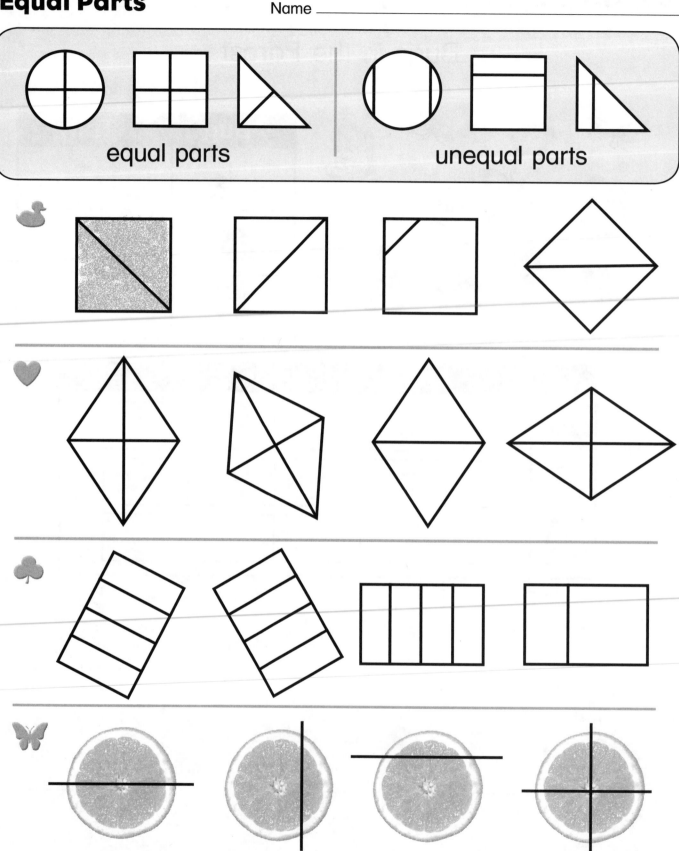

| equal parts | unequal parts |

Directions

🦆 ♥ ♣ Color the figures that have equal parts.

🦋 Circle the figures that show equal parts.

Use with Lesson 6-7, pages 215–216 in the Student Book.
Then go to Lesson 6-8, pages 217–218 in the Student Book.

Explore Symmetry

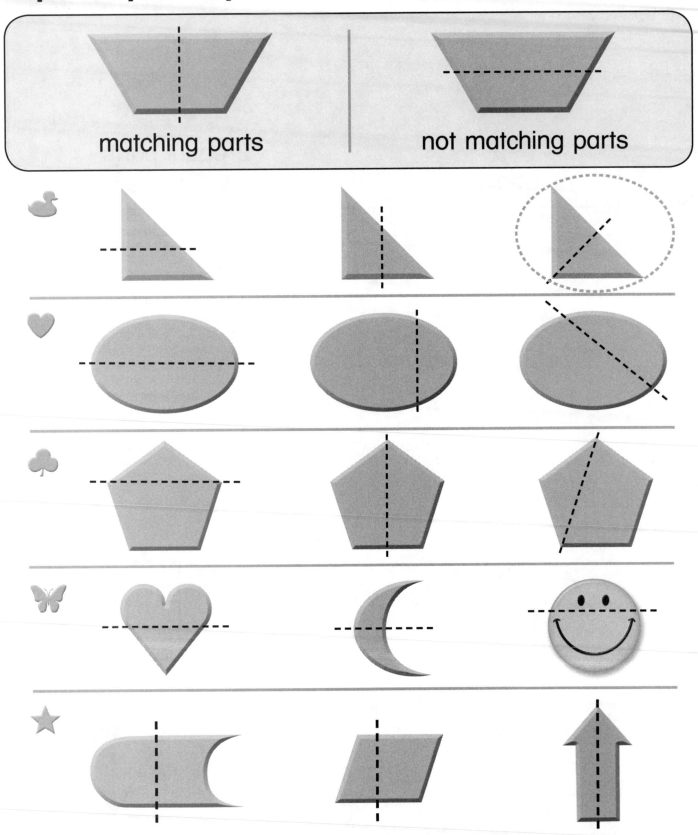

matching parts   not matching parts

Directions

Circle the figure that shows matching parts.

Use with Lesson 6-8, pages 217–218 in the Student Book.
Then go to Lesson 6-9, pages 219–220 in the Student Book.

79

Explore Halves

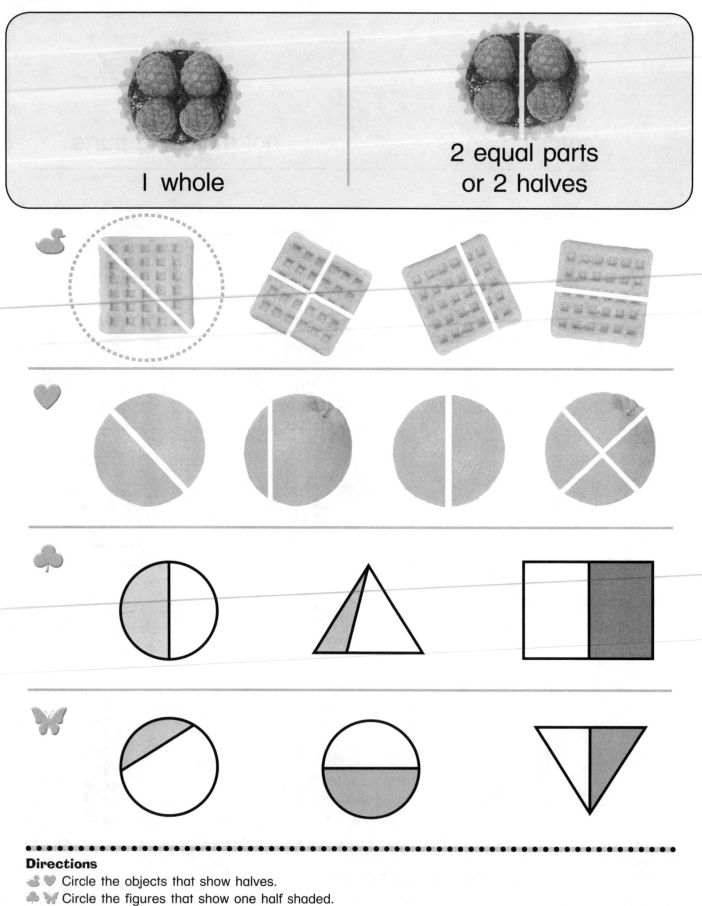

I whole

2 equal parts
or 2 halves

Directions

🦆 💜 Circle the objects that show halves.

♣ 🦋 Circle the figures that show one half shaded.

Use with Lesson 6-9, pages 219–220 in the Student Book.
Then go to Lesson 6-10, pages 221–222 in the Student Book.

Explore Fourths

Name _____

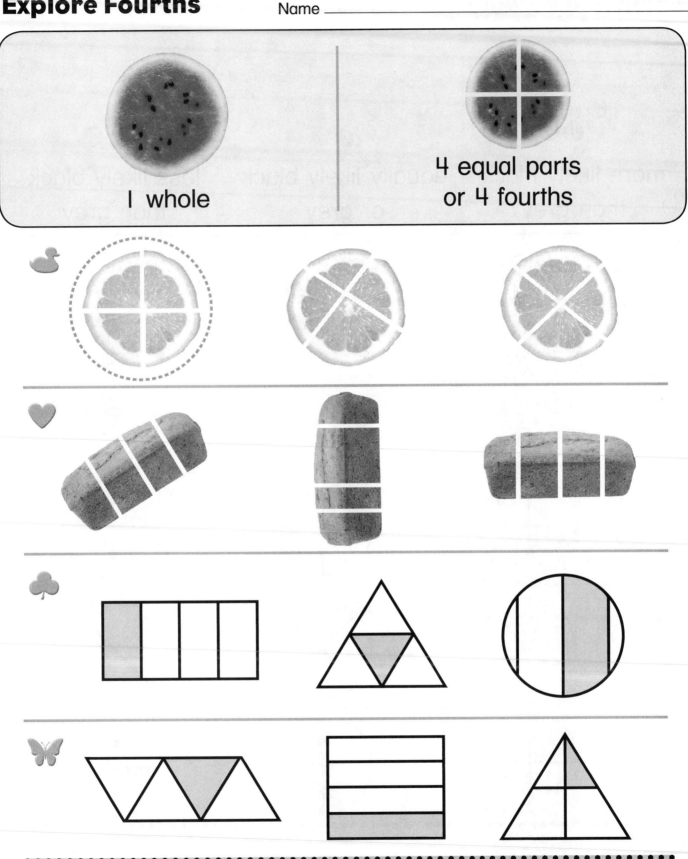

1 whole

4 equal parts
or 4 fourths

- -

Directions
🦆 ❤️ Circle the objects that show fourths.
♣ 🦋 Circle the figures that show one fourth shaded.

Use with Lesson 6-10, pages 221–222 in the Student Book.
Then go to Lesson 6-11, pages 223–224 in the Student Book.

More Likely/Equally Likely/Less Likely

Name _____

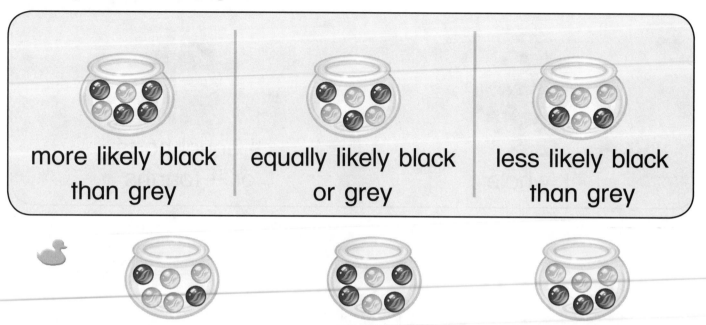

| more likely black than grey | equally likely black or grey | less likely black than grey |

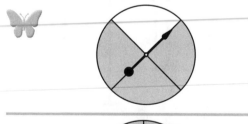 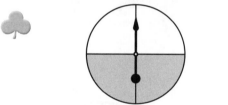    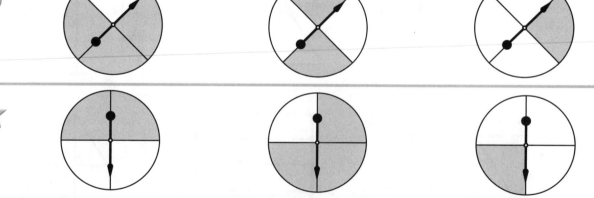

Directions

🦆 Circle the bowl where you are more likely to pick a grey marble.

💜 Circle the bowl where you are less likely to pick a grey marble.

♣ Circle the spinner that is more likely to land on grey.

🦋 Circle the spinner that is less likely to land on grey.

⭐ Circle the spinner that is equally likely to land on grey or white.

Use with Lesson 6-11, pages 223–224 in the Student Book.
Then go to Lesson 6-12, pages 225–226 in the Student Book.

Problem-Solving Strategy:
Make a List

Name _____

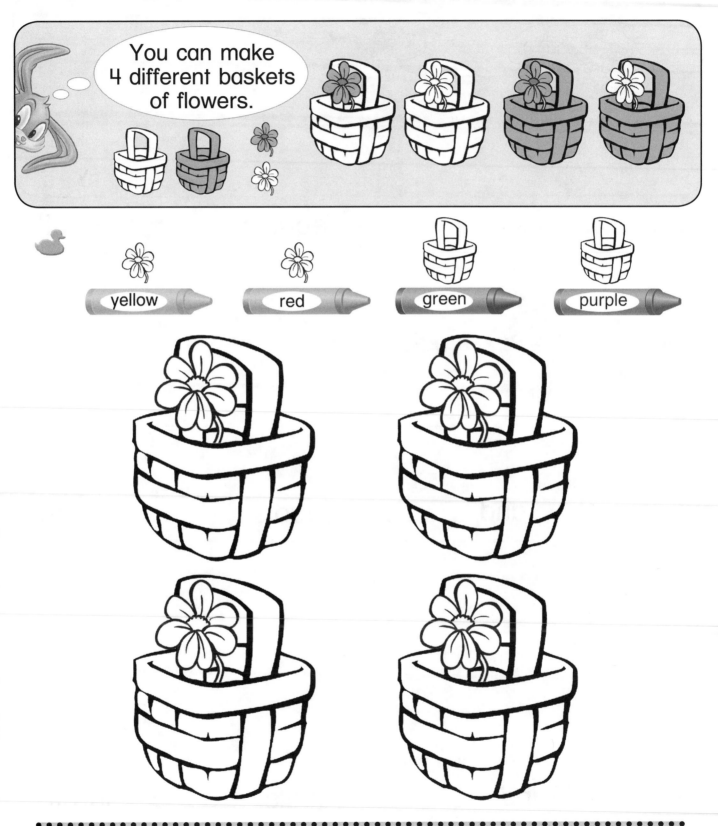

You can make 4 different baskets of flowers.

yellow   red   green   purple

Directions

Color the baskets and flowers to show 4 different ways you can put the flowers into the baskets.

Use with Lesson 6-12, pages 225–226 in the Student Book.

83

Joining

Name _____

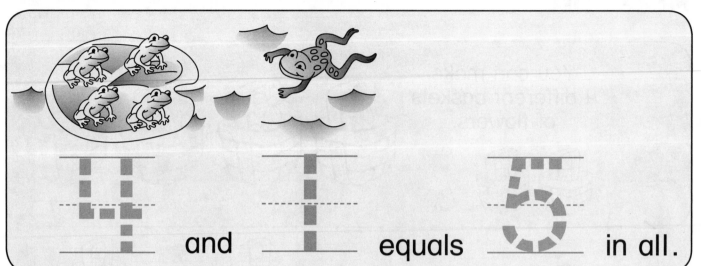

____ and ____ equals ____ in all.

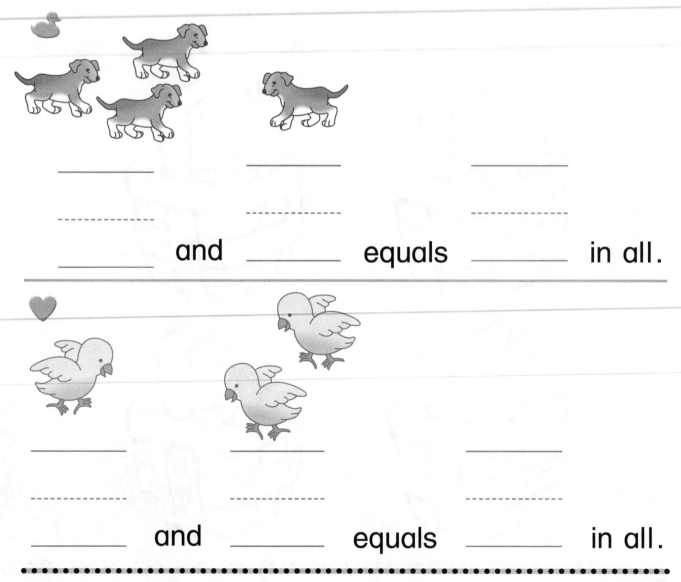

____ and ____ equals ____ in all.

____ and ____ equals ____ in all.

Directions

Write how many are in each part. Then write how many there are in all.

84

Use with Lesson 7-1, pages 237–238 in the Student Book.
Then go to Lesson 7-1A, pages 177–178 in this Workbook.

Add 1

Name _____

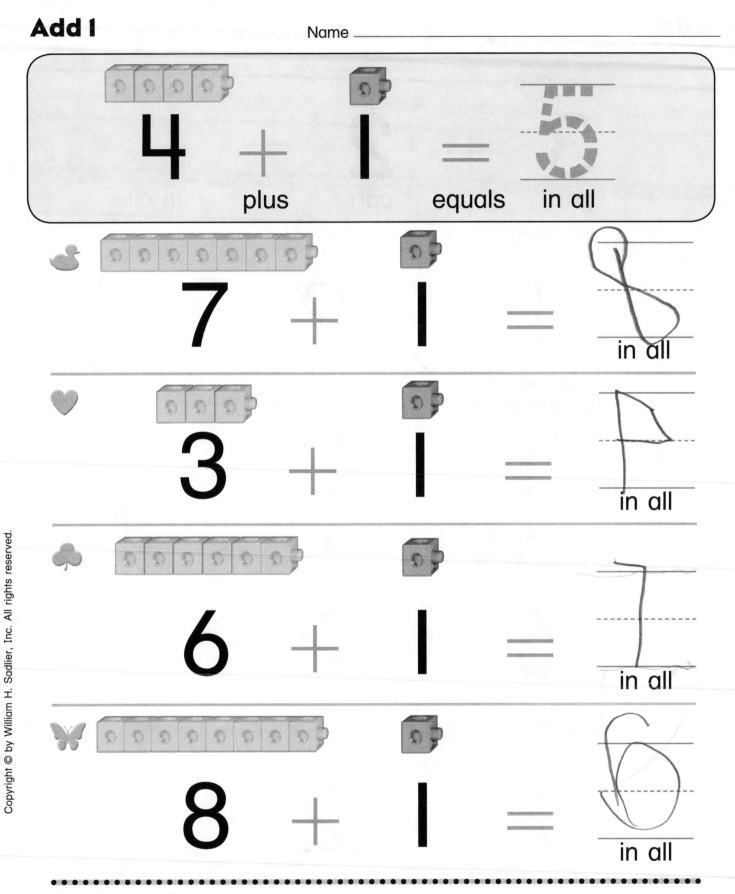

4 + 1 = 5
plus   equals   in all

7 + 1 = _____ in all

3 + 1 = _____ in all

6 + 1 = _____ in all

8 + 1 = _____ in all

•••

Directions
🦆💜♣🦋 Write how many in all.

C Use with Lesson 7-2, pages 239–240 in the Student Book.
C Then go to Lesson 7-3, pages 241–242 in the Student Book.

Add 2

Name _____

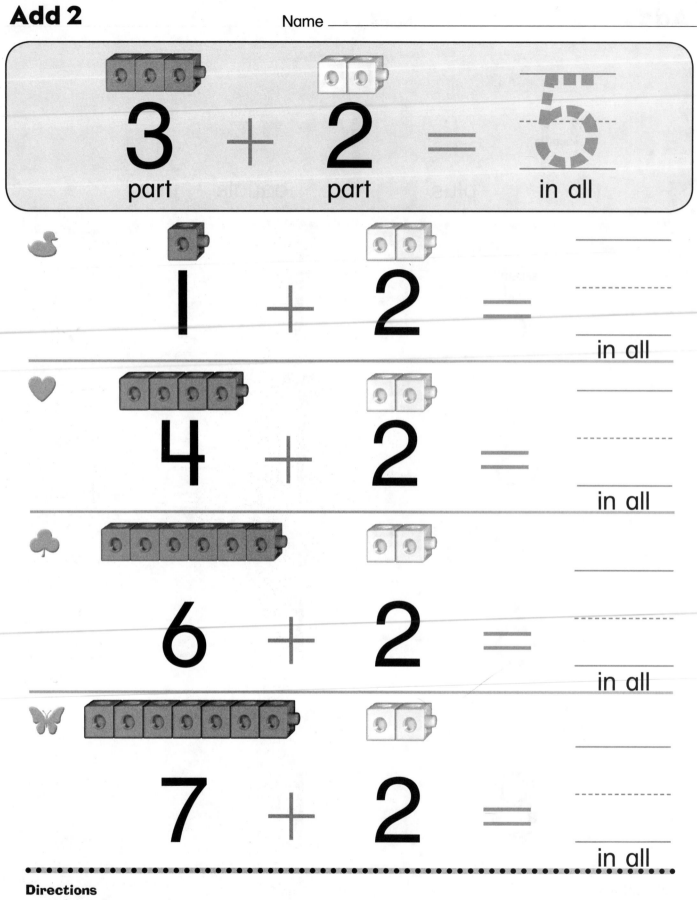

3 + 2 = 5
part   part   in all

🦆   1 + 2 = _____
in all

❤️   4 + 2 = _____
in all

♣️   6 + 2 = _____
in all

🦋   7 + 2 = _____
in all

Directions

🦆❤️♣️🦋 Write how many in all.

86

C Use with Lesson 7-3, pages 241–242 in the Student Book.
C Then go to Lesson 7-4, pages 243–244 in the Student Book.

Add 3

Name _____

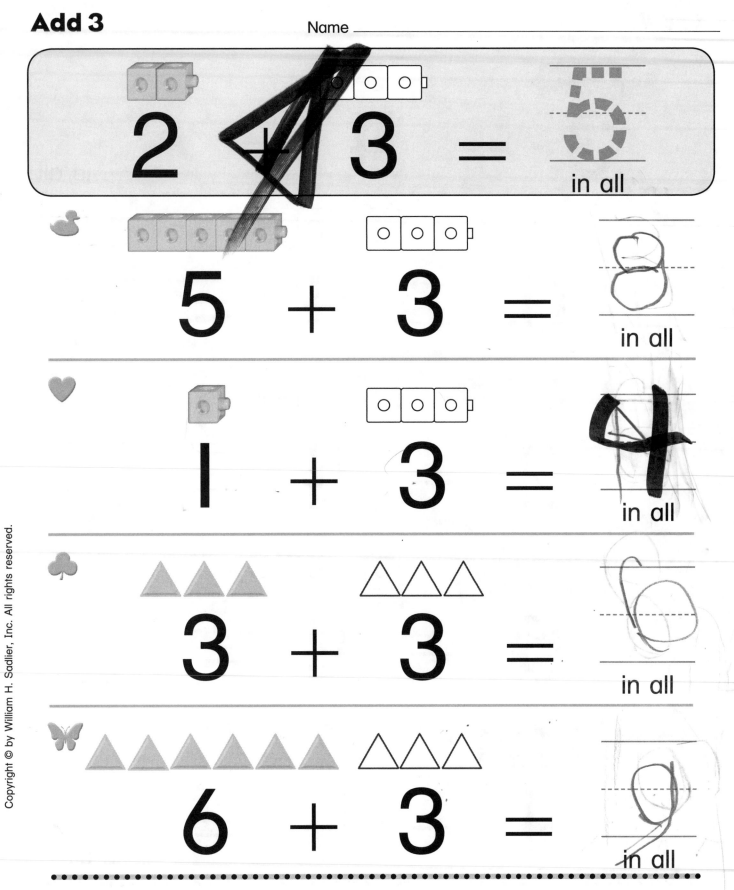

$$2 + 3 = 5 \text{ in all}$$

🦆 $$5 + 3 = 8 \text{ in all}$$

♥ $$1 + 3 = 4 \text{ in all}$$

♣ $$3 + 3 = 6 \text{ in all}$$

🦋 $$6 + 3 = 9 \text{ in all}$$

Directions

🦆 ♥ ♣ 🦋 Color the part joined. Then write how many in all.

C Use with Lesson 7-4, pages 243–244 in the Student Book.
C Then go to Lesson 7-5, pages 245–246 in the Student Book.

Add 4

Name _____

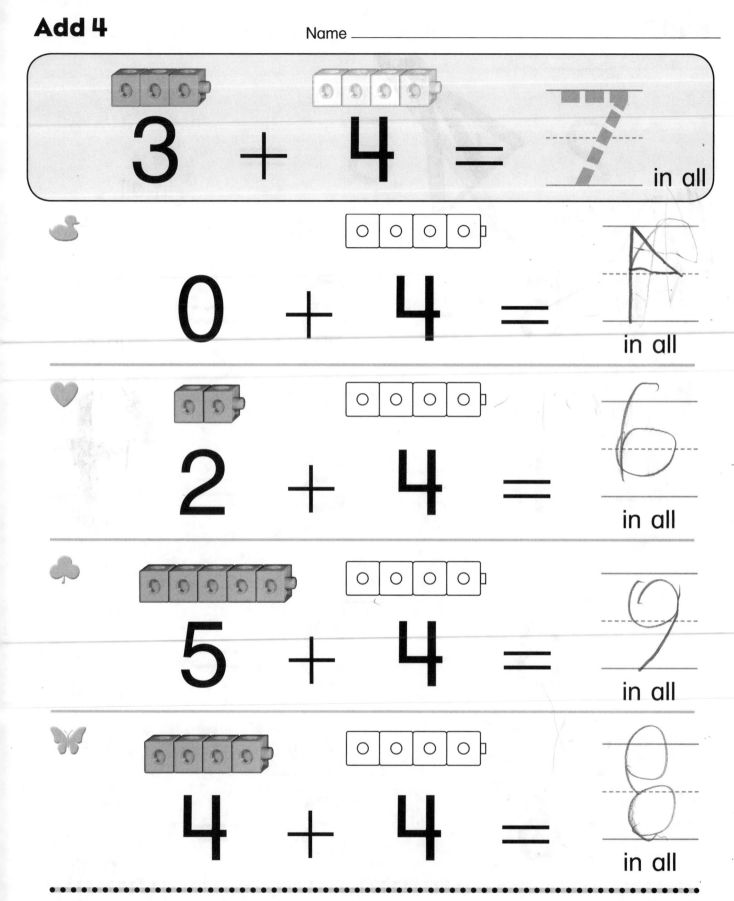

$$3 + 4 = 7 \text{ in all}$$

$$0 + 4 = \underline{} \text{ in all}$$

$$2 + 4 = \underline{6} \text{ in all}$$

$$5 + 4 = \underline{9} \text{ in all}$$

$$4 + 4 = \underline{8} \text{ in all}$$

Directions

Color the part joined. Then write how many in all.

C Use with Lesson 7-5, pages 245–246 in the Student Book.
C Then go to Lesson 7-5A, pages 179–180 in this Workbook.

Vertical Addition

Name _____

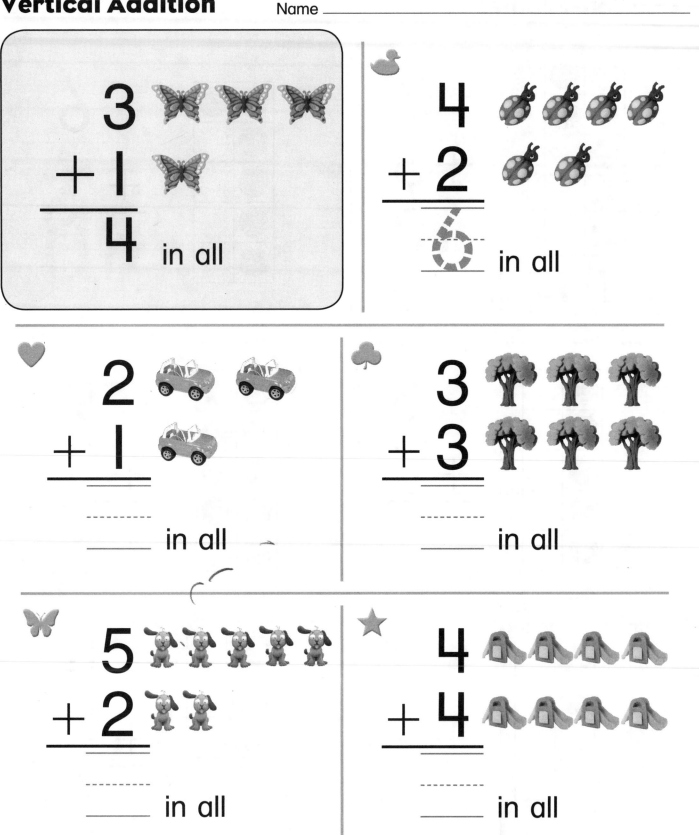

$$3$$
$$+\ 1$$
$$\overline{}$$
$$4$$ in all

$$4$$
$$+\ 2$$
$$\overline{}$$
6 in all

$$2$$
$$+\ 1$$
$$\overline{}$$
___ in all

$$3$$
$$+\ 3$$
$$\overline{}$$
___ in all

$$5$$
$$+\ 2$$
$$\overline{}$$
___ in all

$$4$$
$$+\ 4$$
$$\overline{}$$
___ in all

Directions

Write how many in all.

Use with Lesson 7-6, pages 249–250 in the Student Book.
Then go to Lesson 7-7, pages 251–252 in the Student Book.

Addition:
Use Ten-Frames

Name _____

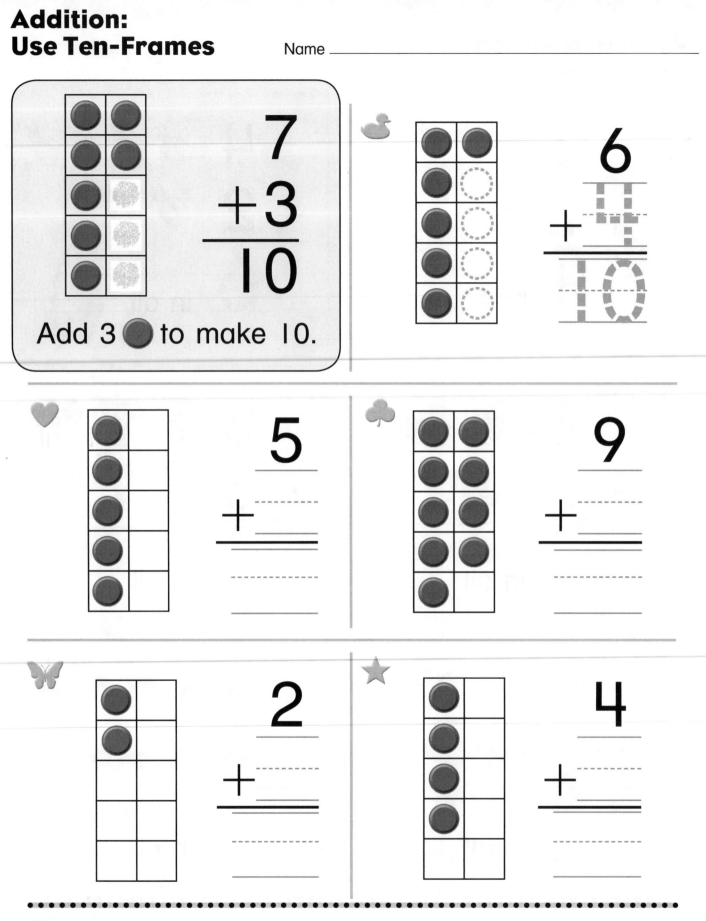

7
+3
10

Add 3 ⬤ to make 10.

6
+
10

5
+

9
+

2
+

4
+

Directions

🦆💜♣🦋⭐ Draw counters to make 10. Write the number.
Then write how many in all.

Ⓒ Use with Lesson 7-7, pages 251–252 in the Student Book.
Ⓒ Then go to Lessons 7-7A, 7-7B, 7-7C, 7-7D, and 7-7E, pages 181–190 in this Workbook.

Problem-Solving Strategy:
Write a Number Sentence

Name _____

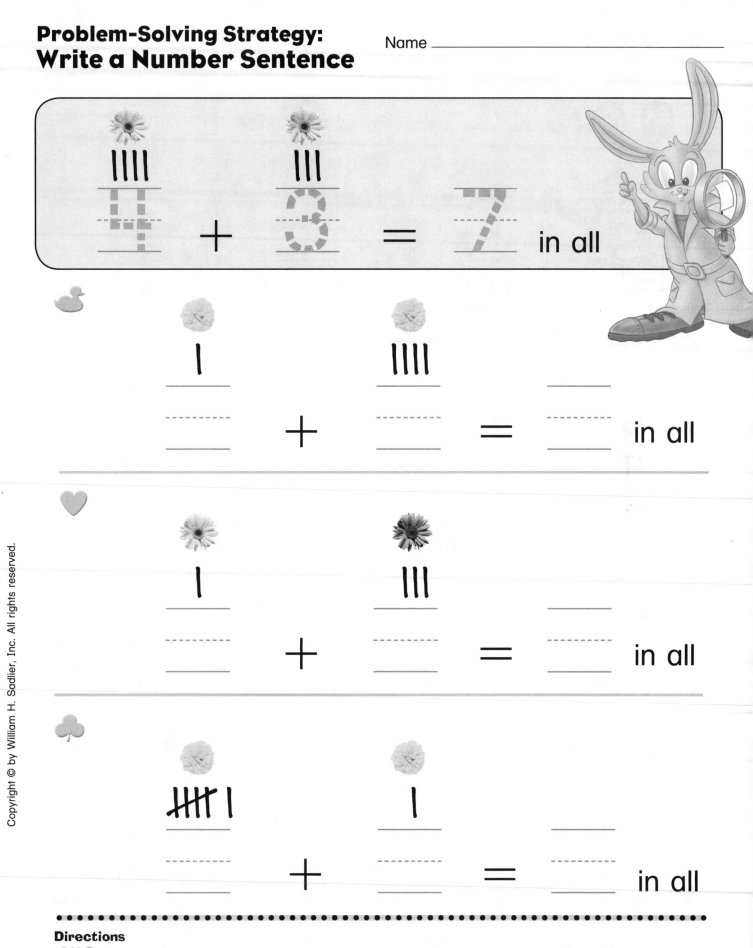

4 + 3 = 7 in all

🦆 ____ + ____ = ____ in all

♥ ____ + ____ = ____ in all

♣ ____ + ____ = ____ in all

Directions
🦆♥♣ Write a number sentence to show how many in all.

🅒 Use with Lesson 7-8, pages 253–254 in the Student Book.

91

Take Away

Name _____

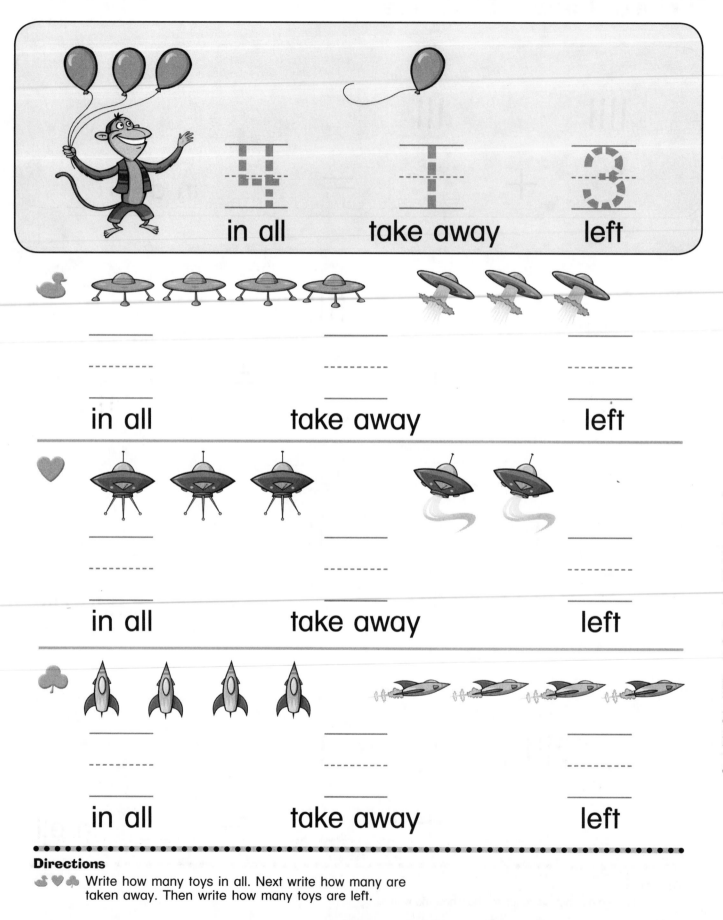

in all　　　take away　　　left

4　　　1　　　3

in all　　　take away　　　left

in all　　　take away　　　left

in all　　　take away　　　left

Directions

♣ ♥ ♣ Write how many toys in all. Next write how many are taken away. Then write how many toys are left.

Use with Lesson 8-1, pages 269–270 in the Student Book.
Then go to Lesson 8-1A, pages 191–192 in this Workbook.

Subtract 1

Name _____

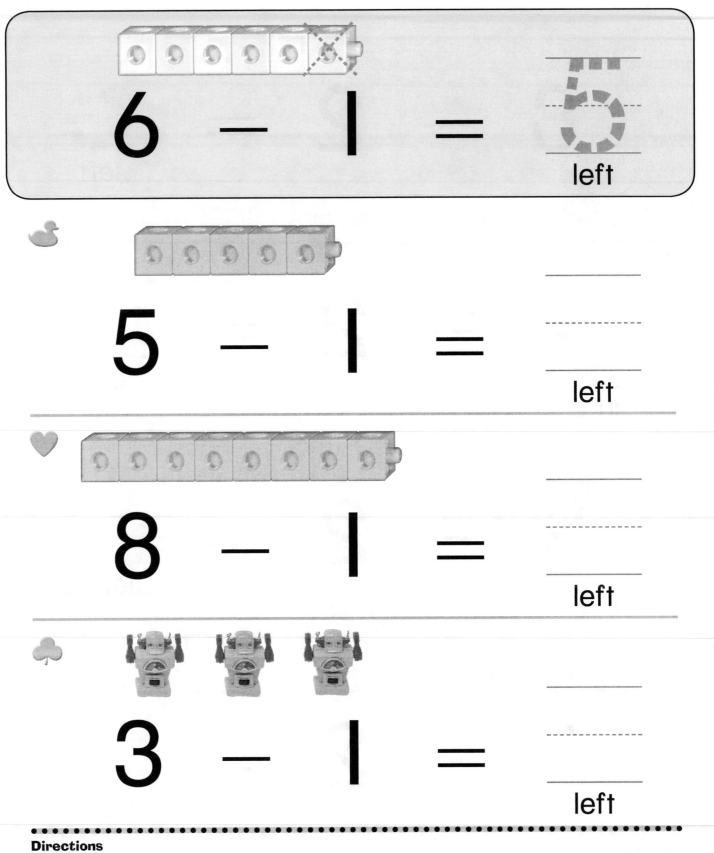

6 – 1 = 5
left

🦆 5 – 1 = _____
left

💜 8 – 1 = _____
left

♣ 3 – 1 = _____
left

Directions

🦆💜 ✗ one cube to subtract 1. Write how many are left.
♣ ✗ one toy to subtract 1. Write how many are left.

C Use with Lesson 8-2, pages 271–272 in the Student Book.
C Then go to Lesson 8-3, pages 273–274 in the Student Book.

Subtract 2

Name _____

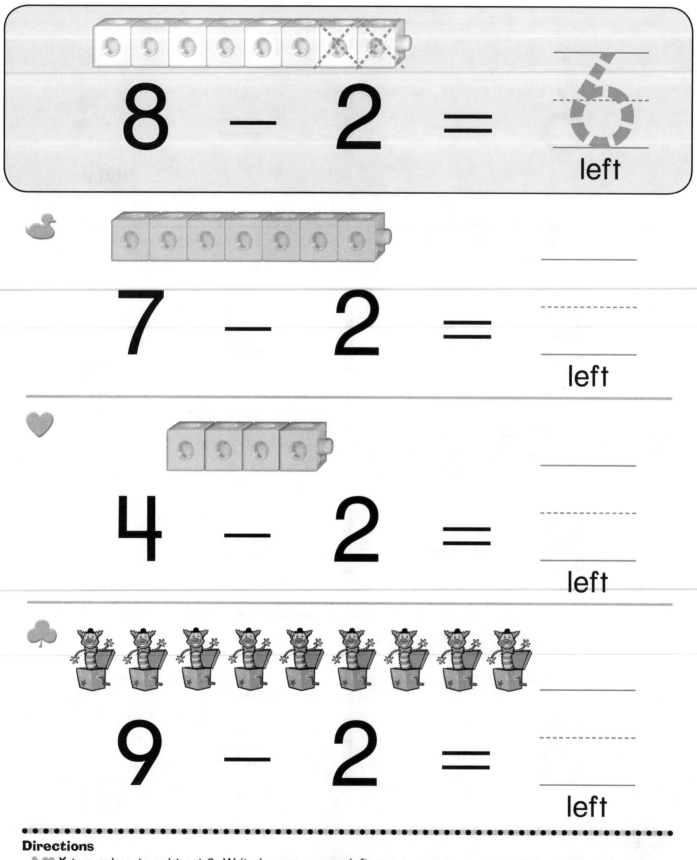

8 – 2 = 6 left

🦆 7 – 2 = _____ left

💜 4 – 2 = _____ left

♣ 9 – 2 = _____ left

Directions
🦆💜✗ two cubes to subtract 2. Write how many are left.
♣✗ two toys to subtract 2. Write how many are left.

94

C Use with Lesson 8-3, pages 273–274 in the Student Book.
C Then go to Lesson 8-4, pages 275–276 in the Student Book.

Subtract 3

Name _____

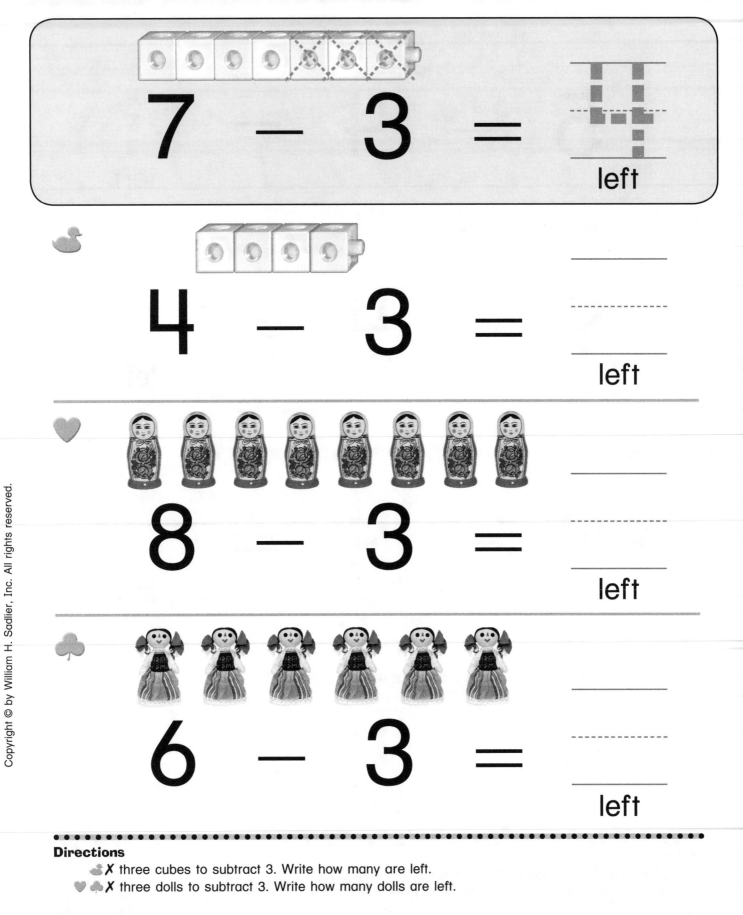

7 − 3 = **4** left

4 − 3 = _____ left

8 − 3 = _____ left

6 − 3 = _____ left

Directions

✗ three cubes to subtract 3. Write how many are left.

✗ three dolls to subtract 3. Write how many dolls are left.

C Use with Lesson 8-4, pages 275–276 in the Student Book.
C Then go to Lesson 8-5, pages 277–278 in the Student Book.

95

Subtract 4

Name _____

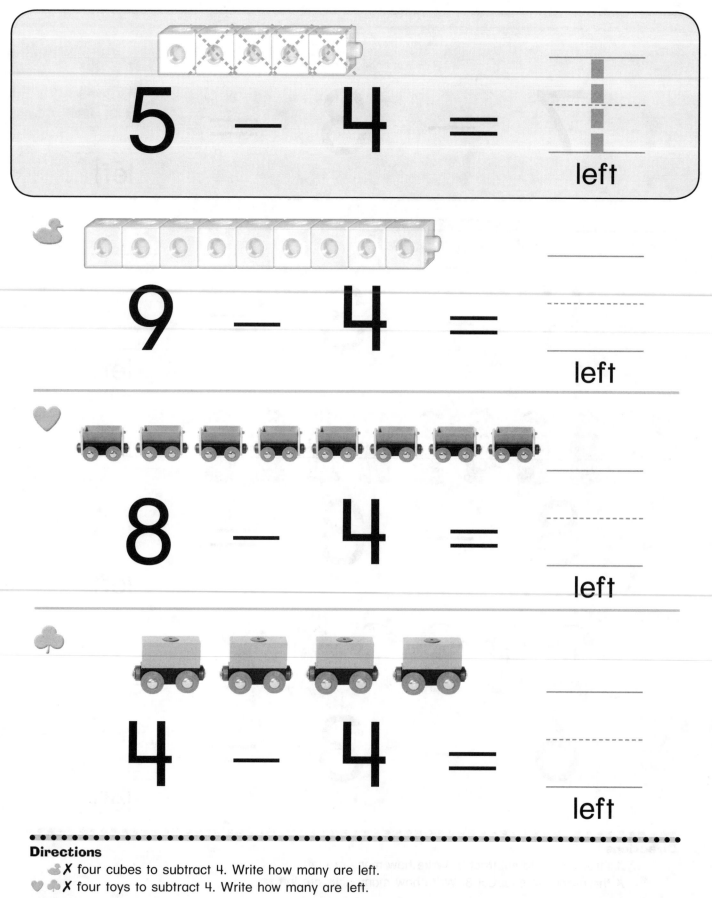

5 − 4 = | left

9 − 4 = ____ left

8 − 4 = ____ left

4 − 4 = ____ left

Directions

🦆 ✗ four cubes to subtract 4. Write how many are left.
♥ ♣ ✗ four toys to subtract 4. Write how many are left.

🅒 Use with Lesson 8-5, pages 277–278 in the Student Book.
🅒 Then go to Lesson 8-5A, pages 193–194 in this Workbook.

Vertical Subtraction   Name _____

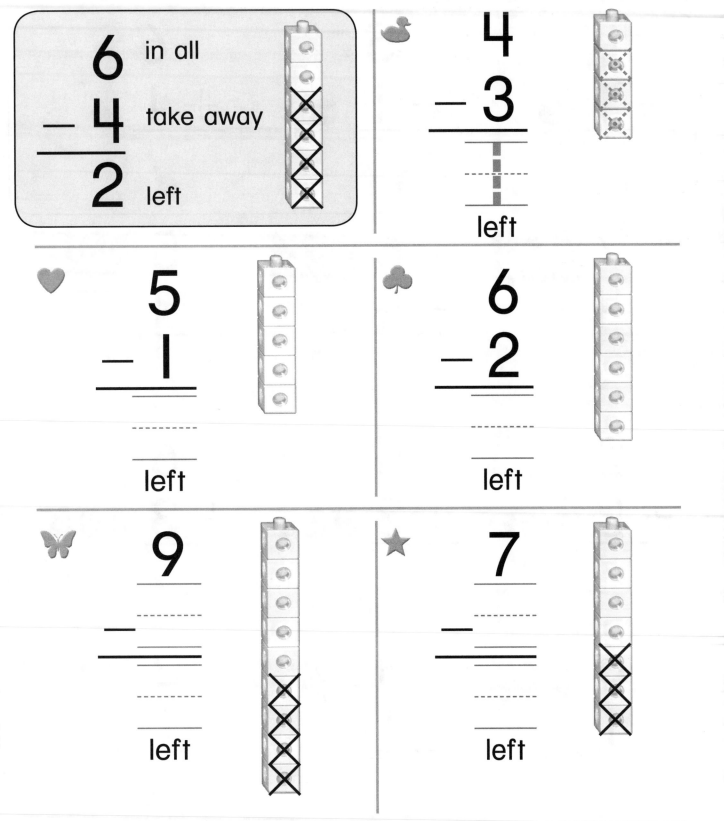

6 in all
− 4 take away
─────
2 left

4
− 3
─────
___ left

5
− 1
─────
___ left

6
− 2
─────
___ left

9
− ___
═════
___ left

7
− ___
═════
___ left

Directions

♣ ♥ ♠ **X** cubes to subtract. Write how many are left.

🦋 ★ Write the number taken away. Then write how many are left.

C Use with Lesson 8-6, pages 281–282 in the Student Book.
C Then go to Lesson 8-7, pages 283–284 in the Student Book.

Addition and
Subtraction Patterns

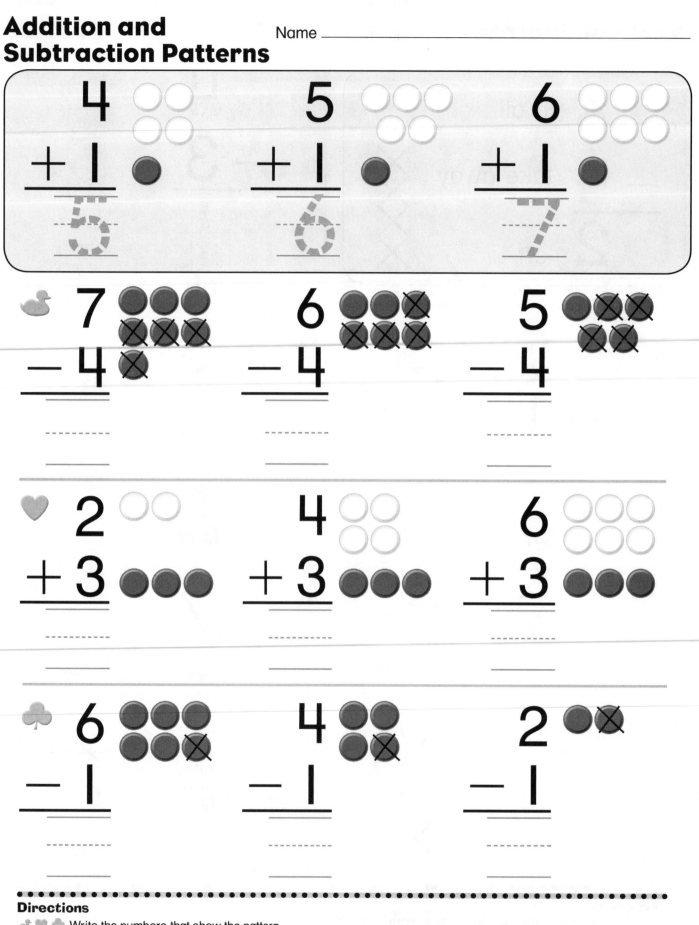

$$4 + 1 = 5$$

$$5 + 1 = 6$$

$$6 + 1 = 7$$

$$7 - 4 =$$

$$6 - 4 =$$

$$5 - 4 =$$

$$2 + 3 =$$

$$4 + 3 =$$

$$6 + 3 =$$

$$6 - 1 =$$

$$4 - 1 =$$

$$2 - 1 =$$

Directions

Write the numbers that show the pattern.

98

© Use with Lesson 8-7, pages 283–284 in the Student Book.
© Then go to Lesson 8-8, pages 285–286 in the Student Book.

Use Ten-Frames to Subtract

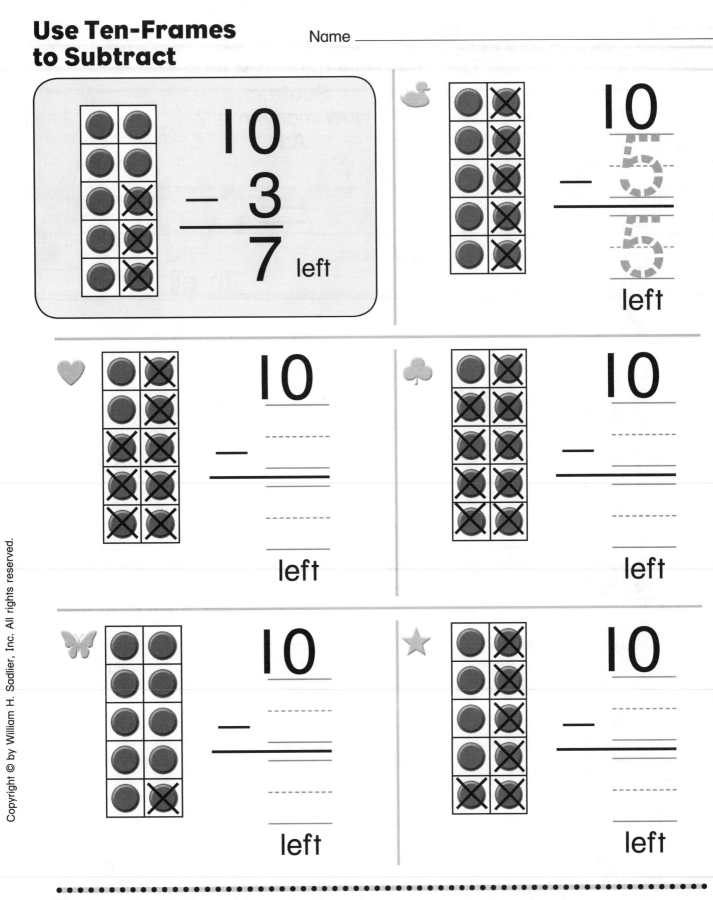

10
− 3
——
7 left

10
− 5
——
5 left

10
− ___
——
___ left

10
− ___
——
___ left

10
− ___
——
___ left

10
− ___
——
___ left

Directions

🦆 ♥ ♣ 🦋 ★ Write how many counters are taken away.
Then write how many are left.

C Use with Lesson 8-8, pages 285–286 in the Student Book.
C Then go to Lesson 8-9, pages 287–288 in the Student Book.

Problem-Solving Strategy: Choose the Operation

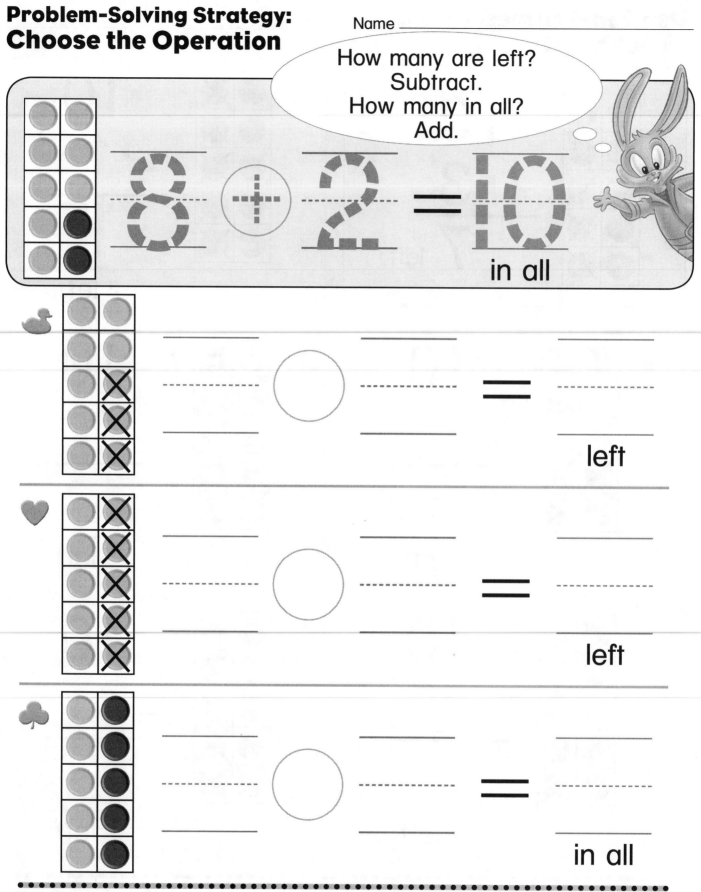

How many are left?
Subtract.
How many in all?
Add.

8 + 2 = 10
in all

_____ ◯ _____ = _____ left

_____ ◯ _____ = _____ left

_____ ◯ _____ = _____ in all

Directions

Look at the ten-frame with counters. Decide whether to add or subtract.
Then write a number sentence to solve.

Use with Lesson 8-9, pages 287–288 in the Student Book.

Pennies and Nickels

Name _____

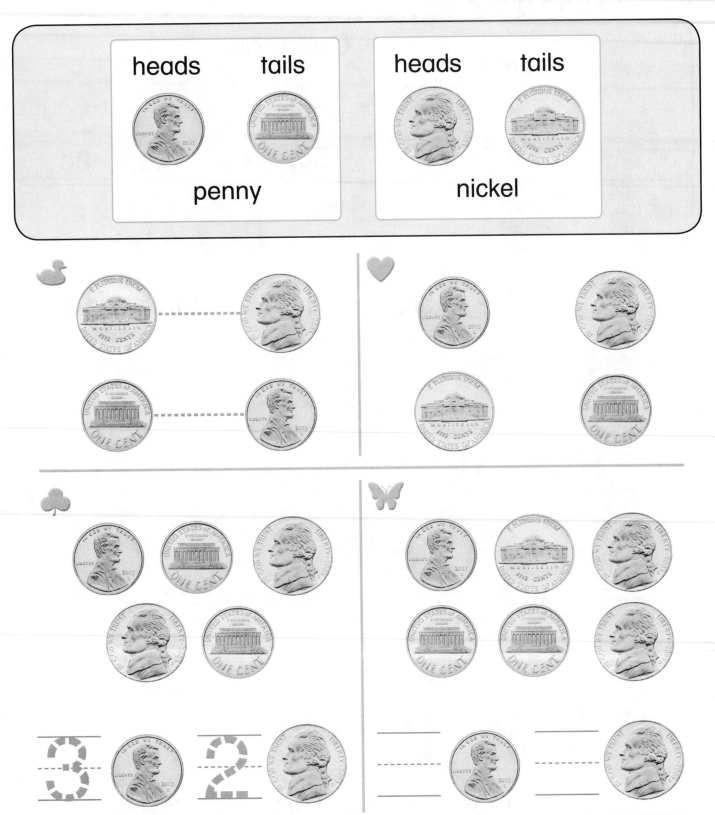

Directions

♣♥ Draw lines to match the two sides of each coin.

♣🦋★✻ Write how many pennies and how many nickels.

C Use with Lesson 9-1, pages 299–300 in the Student Book.
C Then go to Lesson 9-2, pages 301–302 in the Student Book.

101

Count On from Pennies and Nickels

Name _____

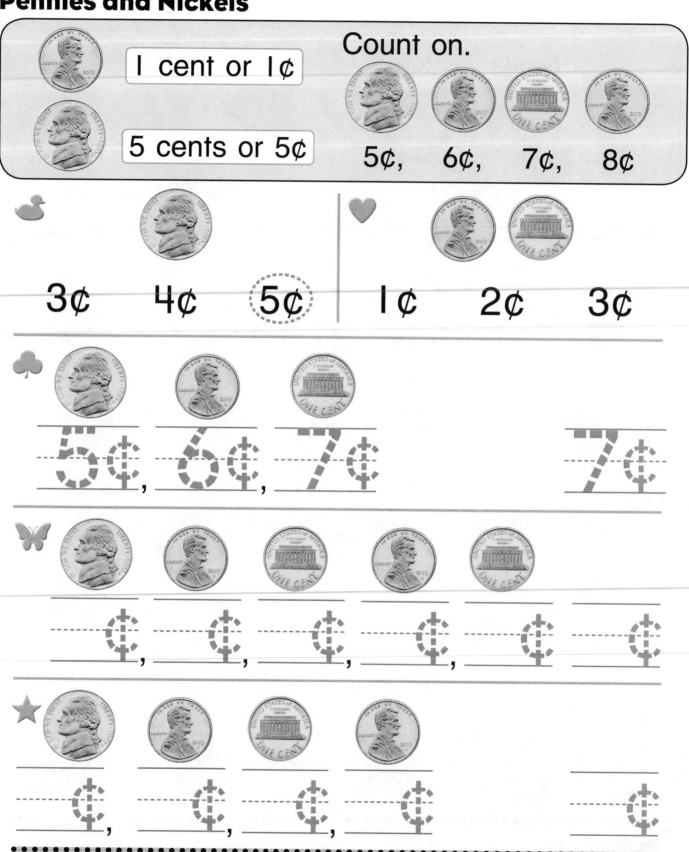

| 1 cent or 1¢ |
| 5 cents or 5¢ |

Count on.

5¢, 6¢, 7¢, 8¢

🦆 3¢   4¢   (5¢)   ❤ 1¢   2¢   3¢

♣ 5¢, 6¢, 7¢   7¢

🦋 ___¢, ___¢, ___¢, ___¢, ___¢

⭐ ___¢, ___¢, ___¢, ___¢

Directions

🦆❤ Count on to find the total. Circle the total amount.
♣🦋⭐ Count on to find the total. Write the total amount.

⊂ Use with Lesson 9-2, pages 301–302 in the Student Book.
⊂ Then go to Lesson 9-3, pages 303–304 in the Student Book.

Dimes and Quarters

Name _____

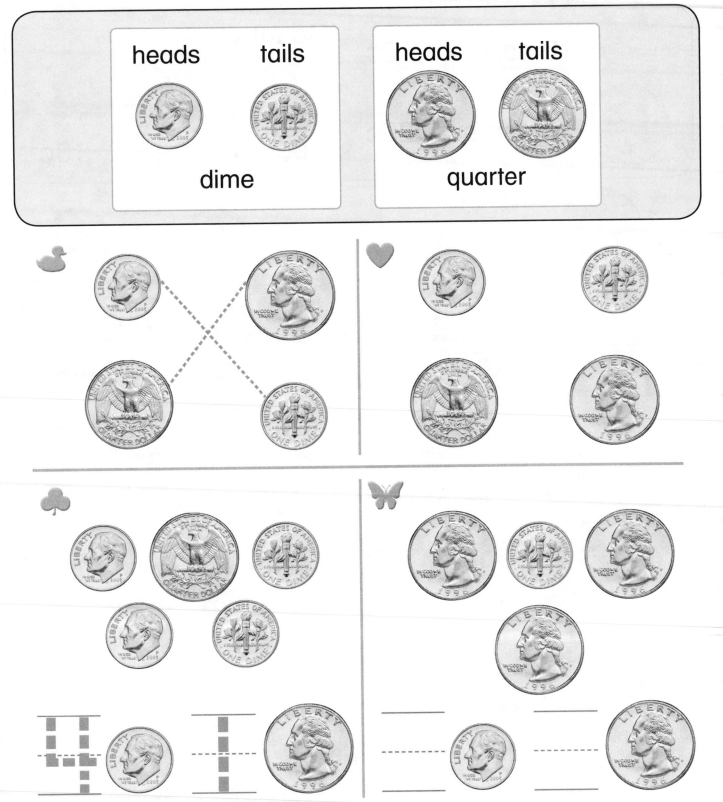

heads   tails   heads   tails

dime   quarter

Directions

🦆💜 Draw lines to match the two sides of each coin.

♣🦋 Write how many quarters and how many dimes.

C Use with Lesson 9-3, pages 303–304 in the Student Book.
C Then go to Lesson 9-4, pages 305–306 in the Student Book.

103

Count On from Dimes and Quarters

10 cents or 10¢

25 cents or 25¢

Count on.

10¢,   11¢,   12¢,   13¢

25¢, 26¢, 27¢, 28¢, 29¢

___¢, ___¢, ___¢, ___¢, ___¢

___¢, ___¢, ___¢, ___¢

___¢, ___¢, ___¢

Directions
Count on to find the total amount.

104

Trading for Nickels

Name _____

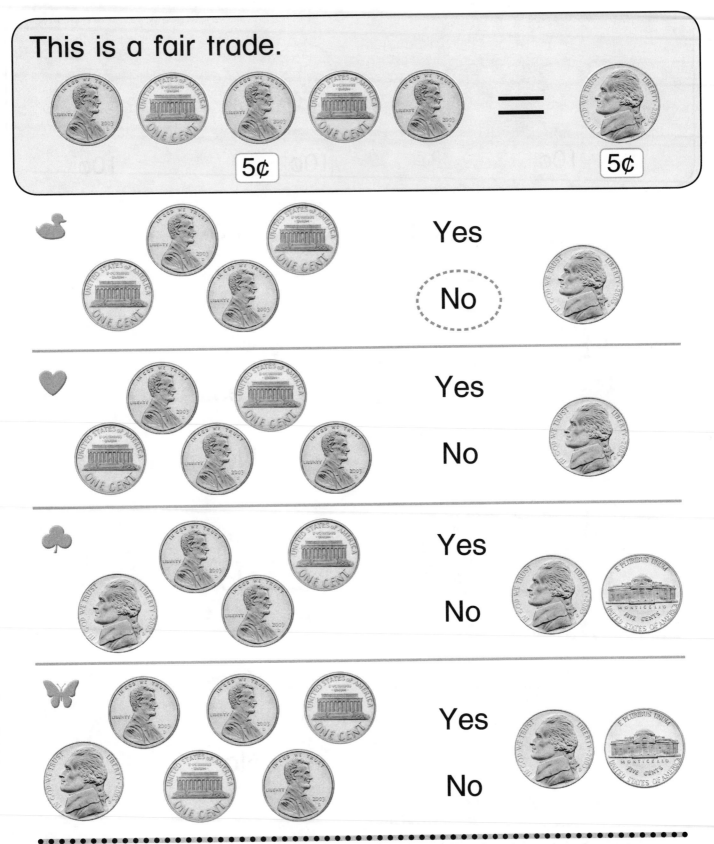

This is a fair trade.

5¢ = 5¢

🦆   Yes   (No)

❤️   Yes   No

♣️   Yes   No

🦋   Yes   No

Directions
🦆❤️♣️🦋 Circle Yes if the amount is a fair trade.
Circle No if the amount is not a fair trade.

Use with Lesson 9-5, pages 309–310 in the Student Book.
Then go to Lesson 9-6, pages 311–312 in the Student Book.

105

Trading for Dimes

Name _____

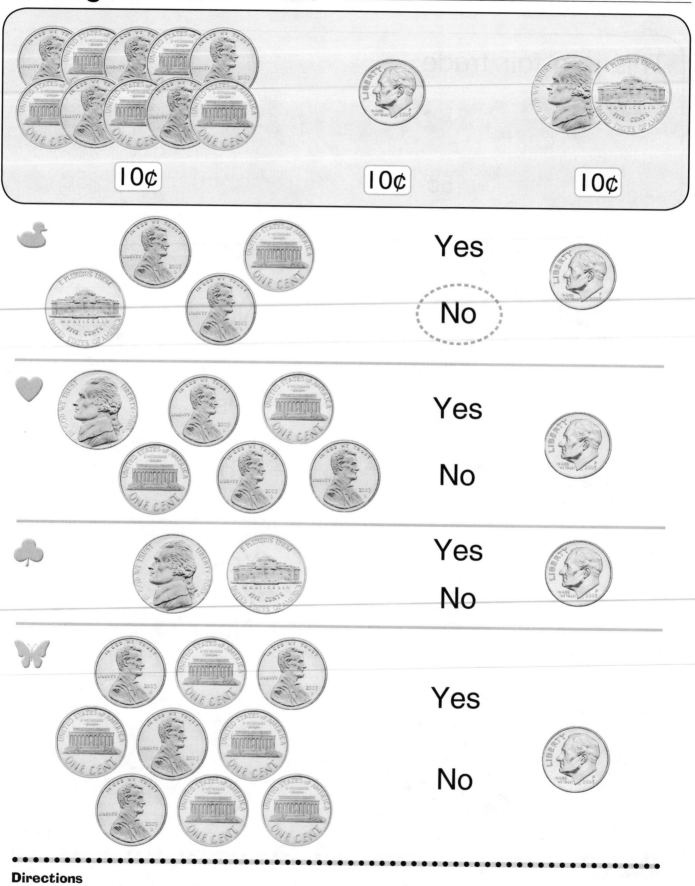

Directions

♣♥♠♥ Circle Yes if the amount is a fair trade.
Circle No if the amount is not a fair trade.

Use with Lesson 9-6, pages 311–312 in the Student Book.
Then go to Lesson 9-7, pages 313–314 in the Student Book.

Comparing Money

Name _____

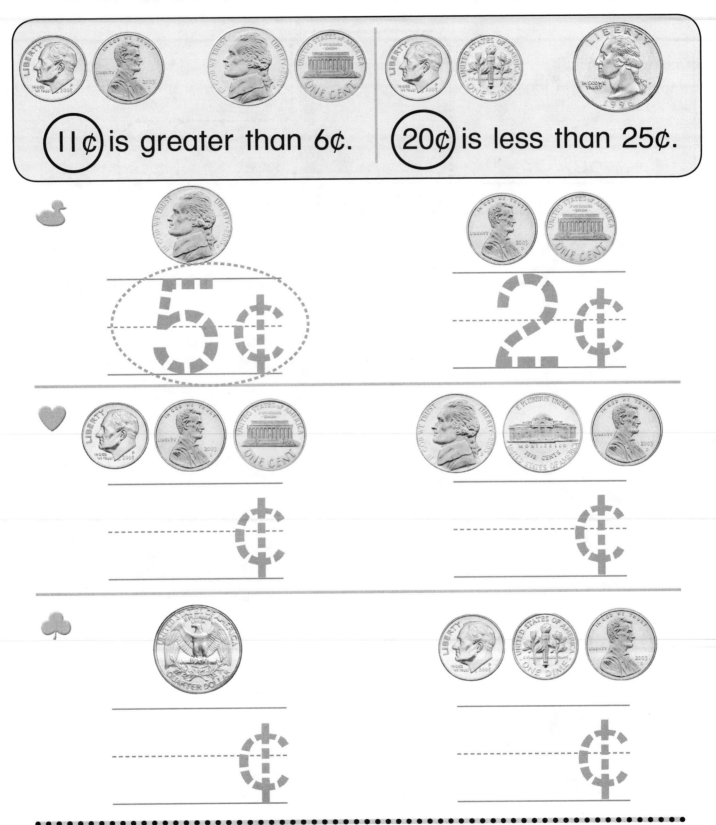

$11¢$ is greater than $6¢$. | $20¢$ is less than $25¢$.

5¢

2¢

_____ ¢   _____ ¢

_____ ¢   _____ ¢

Directions

Write each amount. Circle the amount that is greater.

Write each amount. Circle the amount that is less.

Use with Lesson 9-7, pages 313–314 in the Student Book.
Then go to Lesson 9-8, pages 315–316 in the Student Book.

Using Money

Name _____

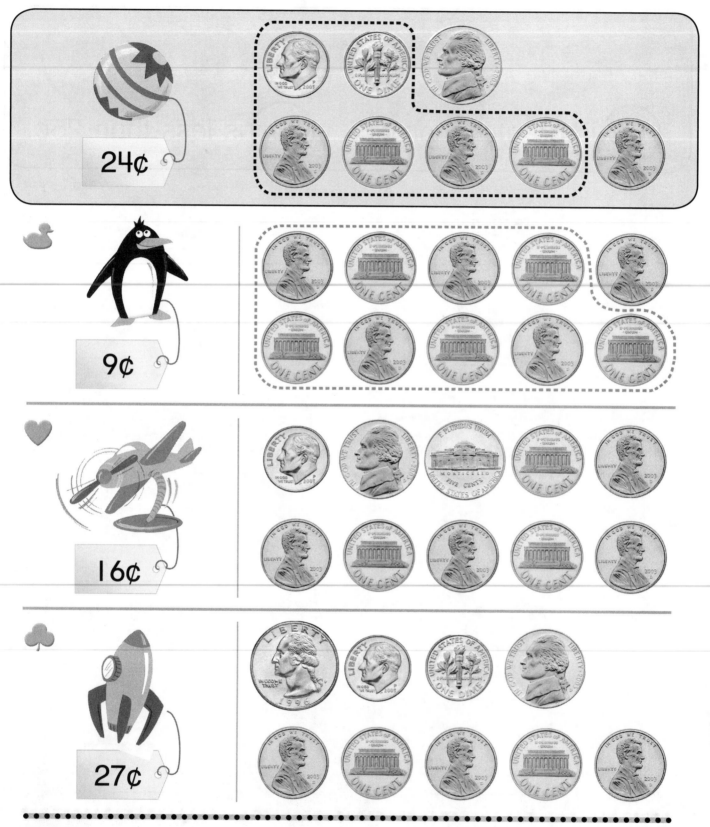

24¢

9¢

16¢

27¢

Directions

♣♥♣ Circle the coins you can use to pay for the item exactly.

Use with Lesson 9-8, pages 315–316 in the Student Book.
Then go to Lesson 9-9, pages 317–318 in the Student Book.

Adding Money

Name _____

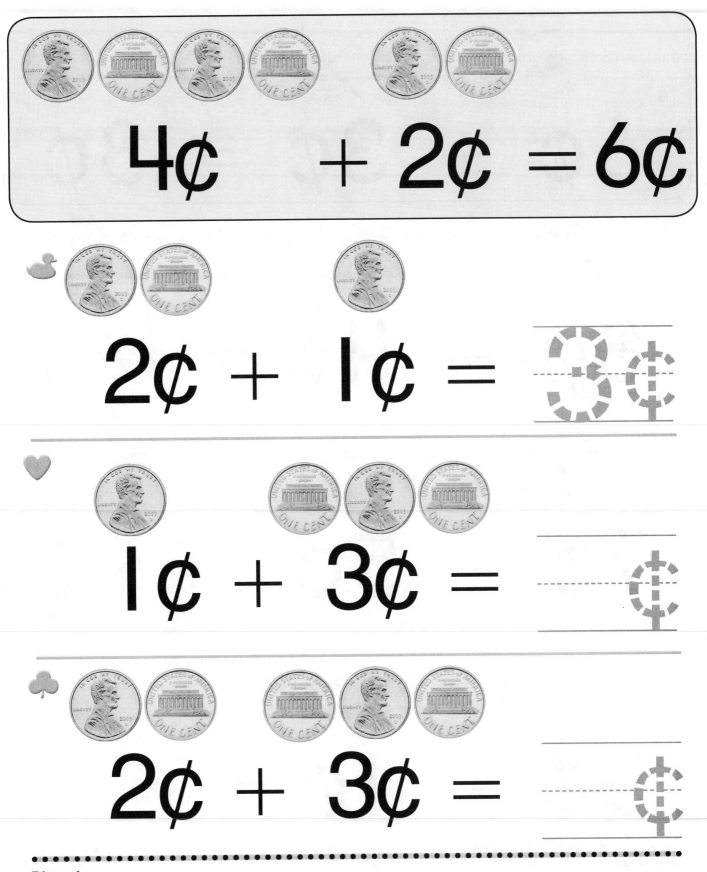

4¢ + 2¢ = 6¢

2¢ + 1¢ = 3¢

1¢ + 3¢ = ___¢

2¢ + 3¢ = ___¢

Directions

Use pennies to model the addition. Write how much in all.

C Use with Lesson 9-9, pages 317–318 in the Student Book.

C Then go to Lesson 9-10, pages 319–320 in the Student Book.

Subtracting Money

Name _____

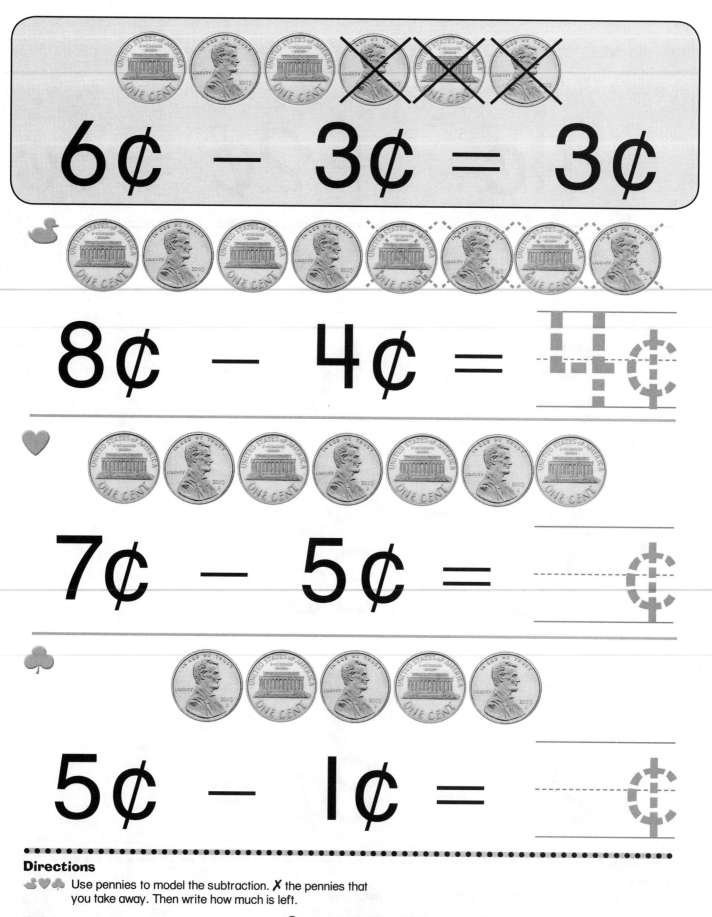

6¢ – 3¢ = 3¢

8¢ – 4¢ = ___¢

7¢ – 5¢ = ___¢

5¢ – 1¢ = ___¢

Directions

Use pennies to model the subtraction. ✗ the pennies that you take away. Then write how much is left.

110

Use with Lesson 9-10, pages 319–320 in the Student Book.
Then go to Lesson 9-11, pages 321–322 in the Student Book.

Problem-Solving Strategy: Use a Model

Name _____

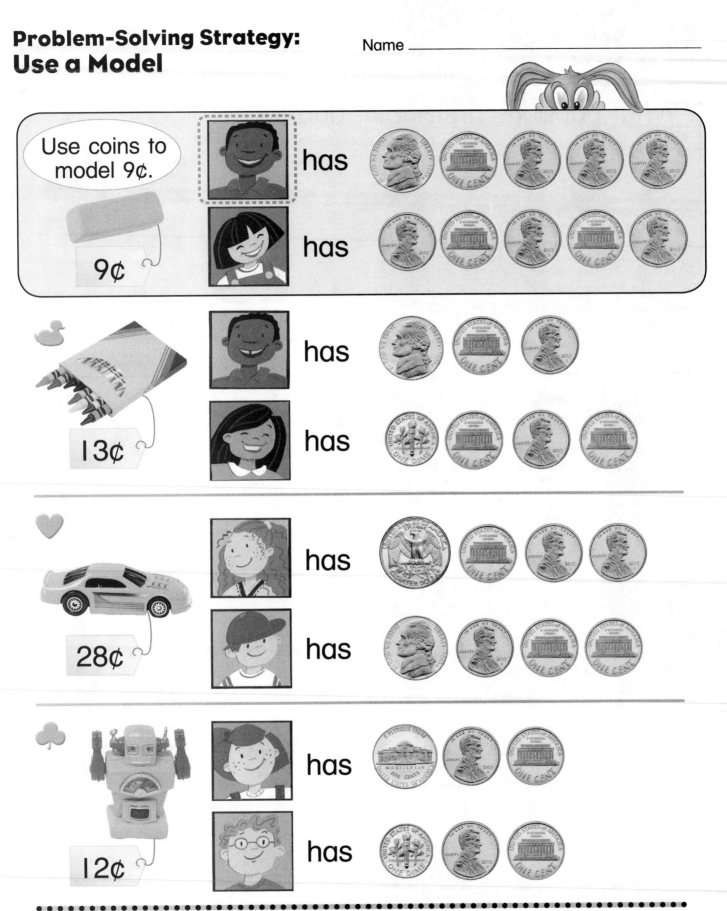

Use coins to model 9¢.

9¢

has

has

13¢

has

has

28¢

has

has

12¢

has

has

Directions

♣ ♥ ♣ Use coins to model the cost of the item.
Circle the person who has enough money to buy the toy.

Use with Lesson 9-11, pages 321–322 in the Student Book.

111

Time Sequence: First, Next, Last

What happens first, next, and last?

Directions

Write 1, 2, and 3 to show what happens first, next, and last.

Use with Lesson 10-1, pages 337–338 in the Student Book.
Then go to Lesson 10-2, pages 339–340 in the Student Book.

Calendar

Name _____

August

Sunday	Monday	Tuesday	Wednesday	Thursday	Friday	Saturday
	1	2	(turtle)	4	5	6
7	-----	(monkey)	-----	11	(fish)	13
-----	15	16	(lizard)	-----		(duck)
21	22	-----	24	(hamster)	-----	27
(dog)	(frog)	(cardinal)	31			

(heart) (frog) __29__ (dog) _____ (duck) _____

(clover) (hamster) _____ (monkey) _____ (lizard) _____

(butterfly) (fish) _____ (cardinal) _____ (turtle) _____

Directions

(duck) Write the missing numbers to complete the calendar. Circle the name of the month. Color red the days of the first week of the month.

(heart)(clover)(butterfly) Write the number for the date each animal is seen.

C Use with Lesson 10-2, pages 339–340 in the Student Book.
C Then go to Lesson 10-3, pages 341–342 in the Student Book.

113

Calendar: Yesterday, Today, Tomorrow

Name _____

🦆

September

Sunday	Monday	Tuesday	Wednesday	Thursday	Friday	Saturday
			1		3	4
	6	7	8		10	
	13			16	17	18
19		21	22		24	
26	27			30		

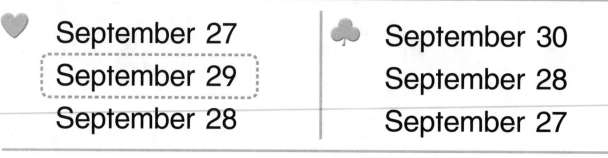

♥ September 27
   September 29
   September 28

♣ September 30
   September 28
   September 27

🦋 Thursday
    Wednesday
    Tuesday

★ Thursday
   Tuesday
   Wednesday

● ●

Directions

🦆 Write the missing dates. Suppose today is September 16. Circle that date in blue, yesterday's date in red, and tomorrow's date in green.

♥ Today is September 28. Circle tomorrow's date.

♣ Today is September 28. Circle yesterday's date.

🦋 Yesterday was Tuesday. What day is it today?

★ Tomorrow is Friday. What day is it today?

114

© Use with Lesson 10-3, pages 341–342 in the Student Book.
Then go to Lesson 10-4, pages 343–344 in the Student Book.

Seasons

Name _____

winter   spring   summer   fall

Directions
🦆 Circle the picture that shows fall.

♥ Circle the picture that shows winter.

♣ Circle the picture that shows spring.

🦋 Circle the picture that shows summer.

Use with Lesson 10-4, pages 343–344 in the Student Book.
Then go to Lesson 10-5, pages 345–346 in the Student Book.

More Time, Less Time

Name _____

more time

less time

SCHOOL BUS

GREEN peas   milk   5.00

Directions

🦆 Circle the activity that takes more time.

💜 Circle the activity that takes less time.

♣ Circle the activity that takes more time.

116

Use with Lesson 10-5, pages 345–346 in the Student Book.
Then go to Lesson 10-6, pages 349–350 in the Student Book.

Time on the Hour

Name _____

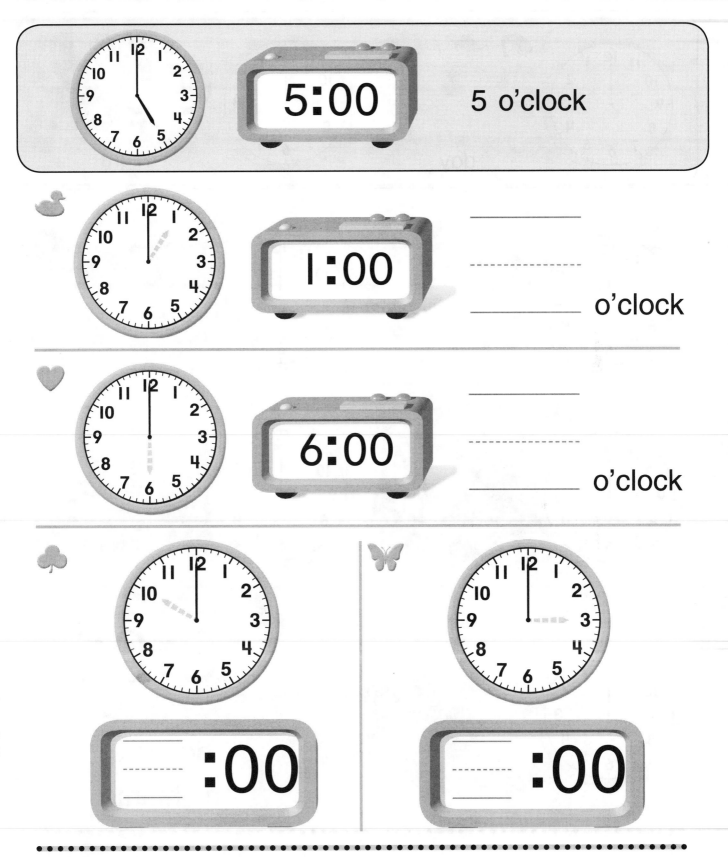

5:00   5 o'clock

🦆   1:00   _____
           - - - - - - - - -
           _____ o'clock

❤️   6:00   _____
           - - - - - - - - -
           _____ o'clock

♣️   ___:00

🦋   ___:00

Directions

🦆❤️♣️🦋 Trace the hour hand. Then read and write the time.

Use with Lesson 10-6, pages 349–350 in the Student Book.
Then go to Lesson 10-7, pages 351–352 in the Student Book.

Tell the Time

Name _____

day

night

3:00

daytime

nighttime

Directions

🦆 ❤️ Trace the hour hand. Circle the daytime activity. ✗ the nighttime activity.

♣ Draw the hour hand to match the time on the other clock. Circle daytime or nighttime to show when what is shown in the picture might happen.

Use with Lesson 10-7, pages 351–352 in the Student Book.
Then go to Lesson 10-8, pages 353–354 in the Student Book.

Problem-Solving Strategy: Use a Model

Name _____

10:00 — day / (night)	**1:00** — morning / (afternoon) / evening
7:00 — day / night	**3:00** — morning / afternoon / evening
8:00 — morning / afternoon / evening	**8:00** — morning / afternoon / evening

Directions

🦆 Draw the hour hand to match the time on the other clock.
Circle to show if the event takes place during the day or at night.

♥♣🦋 Draw the hour hand to match the time on the other clock.
Circle to show the time as morning, afternoon, or evening.

Use with Lesson 10-8, pages 353–354 in the Student Book.

119

Compare by Size

Name _____

smaller   larger

Directions

♣ ♥ ♣ ▶ ★ ✿ Think about these real objects. ✗ the object
that is smaller. Circle the object that is
larger.

120

☞ Use with Lesson 11-1, pages 365–366 in the Student Book.
☞ Then go to Lesson 11-2, pages 367–368 in the Student Book.

Compare by Length

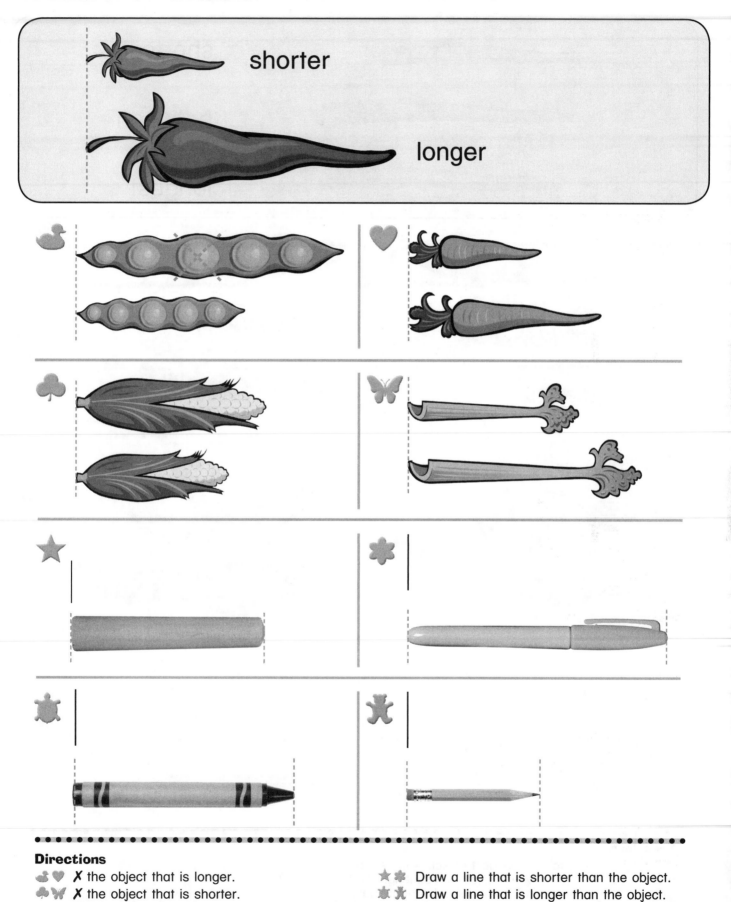

shorter

longer

Directions

🦆❤ **X** the object that is longer.

♣🦋 **X** the object that is shorter.

⭐✿ Draw a line that is shorter than the object.

🐢🐻 Draw a line that is longer than the object.

C Use with Lesson 11-2, pages 367–368 in the Student Book.

C Then go to Lesson 11-3, pages 369–370 in the Student Book.

Order by Length

Name _____

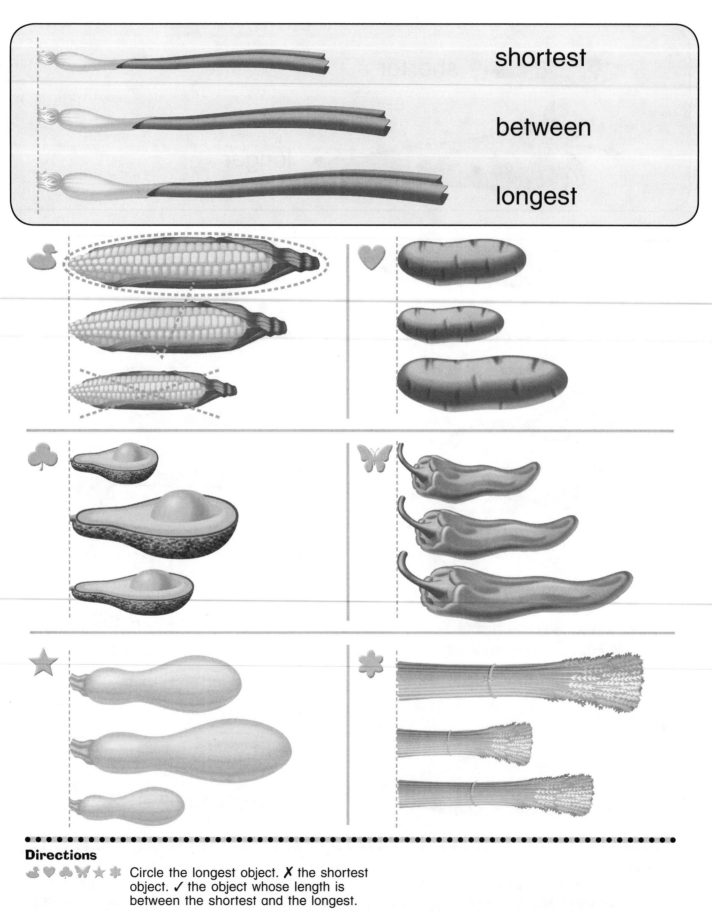

	shortest
	between
	longest

Directions

♣ ♥ ♠ 🦋 ★ ✿ Circle the longest object. ✗ the shortest object. ✓ the object whose length is between the shortest and the longest.

122

© Use with Lesson 11-3, pages 369–370 in the Student Book.
© Then go to Lesson 11-4, pages 371–372 in the Student Book.

Compare by Height

Name _____

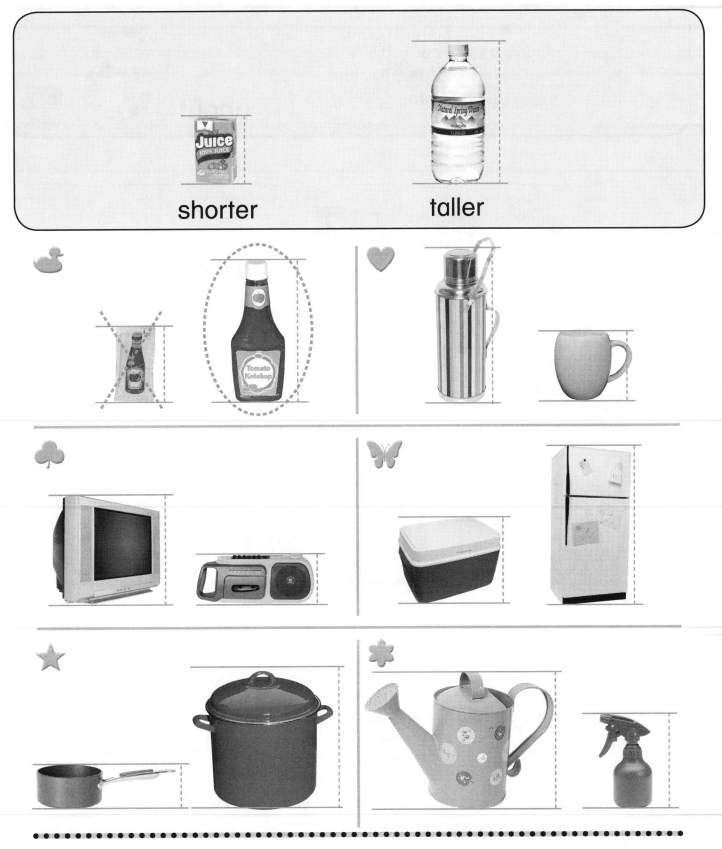

shorter   taller

Directions

Think about these real objects. Circle the object
that is taller. ✗ the object that is shorter.

Use with Lesson 11-4, pages 371–372 in the Student Book.
Then go to Lesson 11-5, pages 373–374 in the Student Book.

123

Measure Length

Name _____

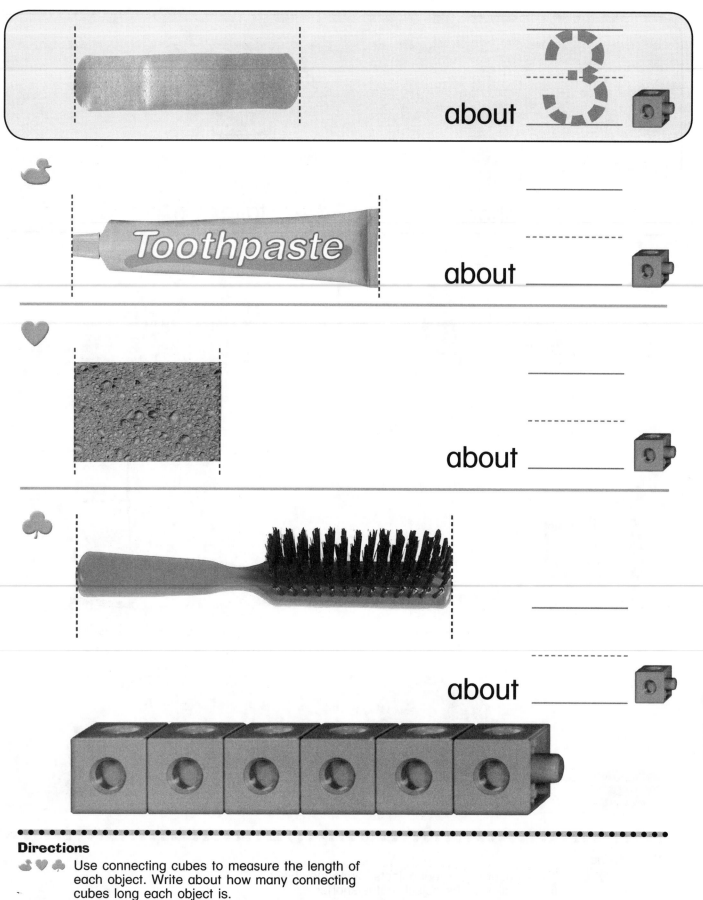

about _3_

about _____

about _____

about _____

Directions

Use connecting cubes to measure the length of each object. Write about how many connecting cubes long each object is.

124

Use with Lesson 11-5, pages 373–374 in the Student Book.
Then go to Lesson 11-6, pages 375–376 in the Student Book.

Measure Distance Around

Name _____

about __6__ 🖇

🦆

about _____ 🖇

♥

about _____ 🖇

♣

about _____ 🖇

Directions

🦆 ♥ ♣ Use small paper clips to measure the
distance around the figure.

C Use with Lesson 11-6, pages 375–376 in the Student Book.
C Then go to page 126 in this Workbook.

125

Measure Distance Around

Name _____

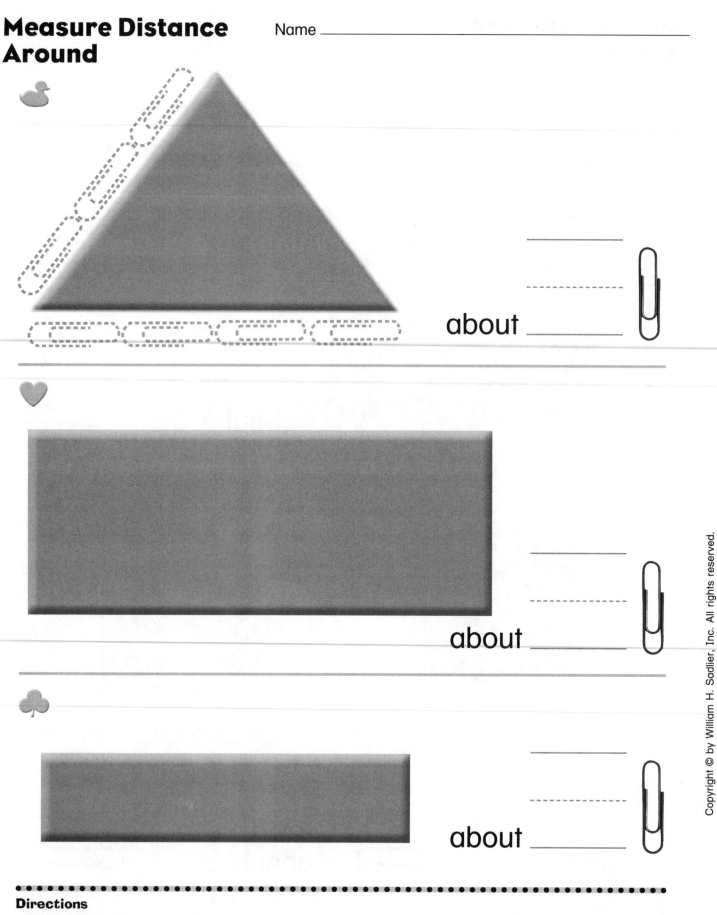

about _____

about _____

about _____

Directions

🦆 ♥ ♣ Use small paper clips to measure the distance around the figure.

126

Ⓒ Use with Lesson 11-6, pages 375–376 in the Student Book.
Ⓒ Then go to Lesson 11-7, pages 379–380 in the Student Book.

Weight: Heavier or Lighter

Name _____

heavier   lighter

Directions Think about these real objects.

Draw a line from the object to the empty side of the balance to make the balance true.

Circle the object that is heavier.
X the object that is lighter.

C Use with Lesson 11-7, pages 379–380 in the Student Book.
C Then go to Lesson 11-8, pages 381–382 in the Student Book.

127

Order by Weight

Name _____

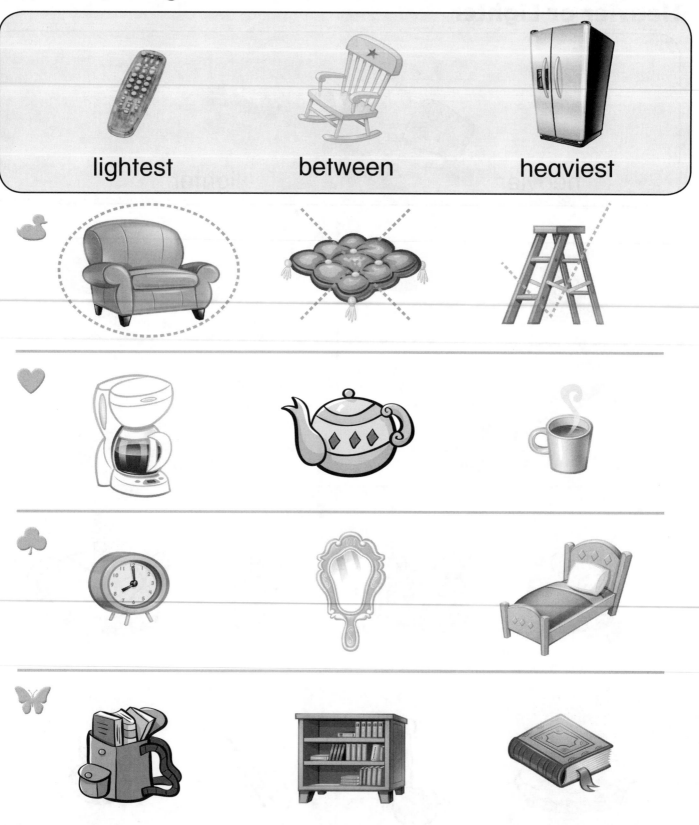

lightest · between · heaviest

Directions

🍀 ♥ ♣ 🦋 Think about these real objects. ✗ the lightest object. Circle the heaviest object. ✓ the object whose weight is between the heaviest and the lightest.

128

🅒 Use with Lesson 11-8, pages 381–382 in the Student Book.
🅒 Then go to Lesson 11-9, pages 383–384 in the Student Book.

Holds More or Holds Less

Name _____

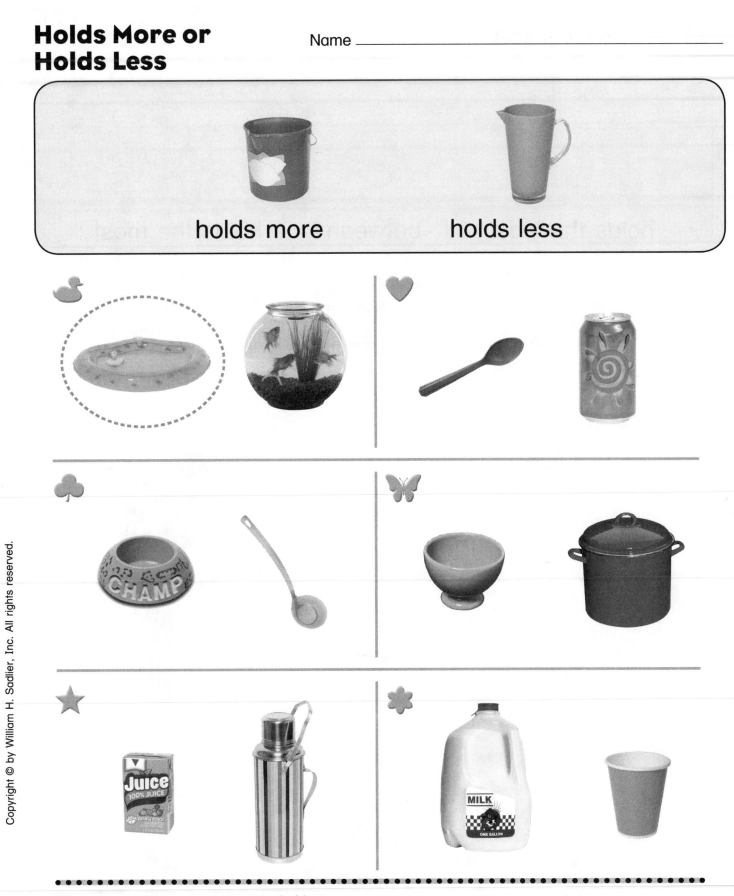

holds more   holds less

Directions   Think about these real objects.

🦆💜♣ Circle the object that holds more.

🦋⭐✿ ✗ the object that holds less.

🇨 Use with Lesson 11-9, pages 383–384 in the Student Book.
🇨 Then go to Lesson 11-10, pages 385–386 in the Student Book.

129

Order by Capacity

Name _____

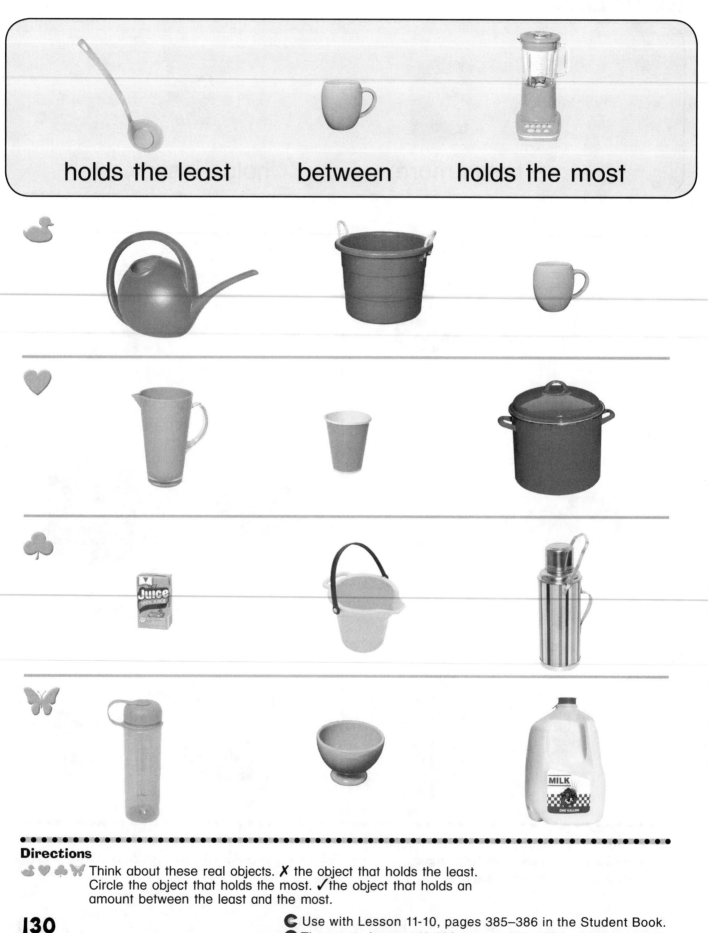

holds the least   between   holds the most

Directions

Think about these real objects. ✗ the object that holds the least. Circle the object that holds the most. ✓ the object that holds an amount between the least and the most.

130

Use with Lesson 11-10, pages 385–386 in the Student Book.
Then go to Lesson 11-10A, pages 195–196 in this Workbook.

Temperature

Name _____

cold   hot

hot   (cold)

hot   cold

hot   cold

hot   cold

hot   cold

hot   cold

Directions

Circle the temperature.

Use with Lesson 11-11, pages 387–388 in the Student Book.
Then go to Lesson 11-12, pages 389–390 in the Student Book.

131

Problem-Solving Strategy:
Make a Graph

Name _____

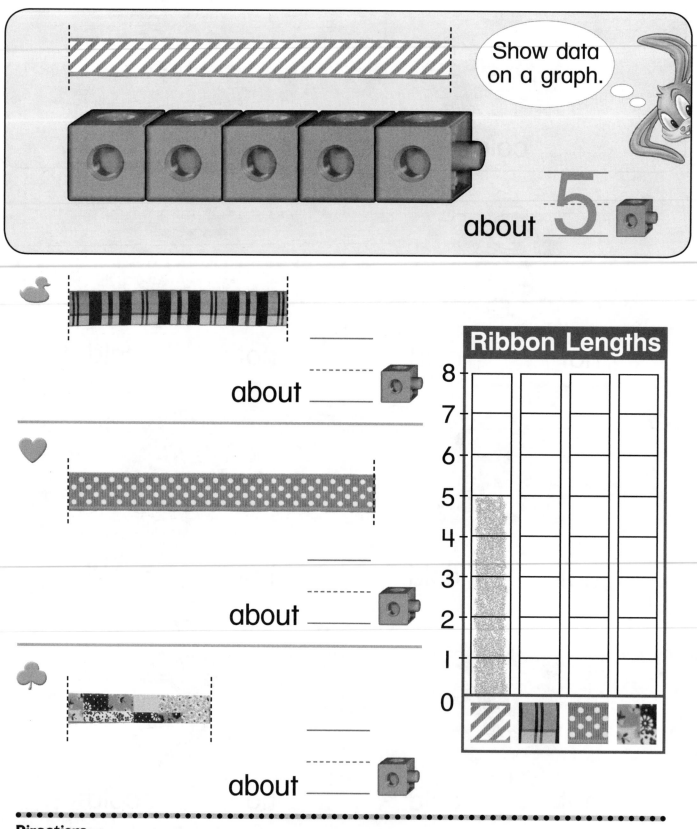

Show data on a graph.

about ___5___

Ribbon Lengths

about _____

about _____

about _____

about _____

about _____

8
7
6
5
4
3
2
1
0

•••••••••••••••••••••••••••••••••••••••

Directions

Use the cubes at the top of the page to measure the length of the ribbon.
Then record the length on the graph. Color one box for each cube.

Use with Lesson 11-12, pages 389–390 in the Student Book.

Count to 100

1	2	3	4	5	6	7	8	9	10
11	12	13	14	15	16	17	18	19	20
21		23	24	25	26	27	28	29	30
31	32	33	34	35		37	38	39	40
41	42	43	44	45	46	47	48	49	50
51	52	53		55	56	57		59	60
61	62		64	65	66	67	68		70
	72	73	74	75	76	77	78	79	
81	82	83	84	85	86		88	89	90
91	92	93	94		96	97	98	99	100

_____, 58, 59, _____, _____, 62, 63

64, 65, 66, _____, _____, 68, 69, _____

Directions

🦆 Count from 1 to 100. Complete the hundred chart.

💜♣ Use the hundred chart to find the missing numbers. Write the numbers.

C Use with Lesson 12-1, pages 405–406 in the Student Book.

C Then go to Lesson 12-1A and 12-1B, pages 197–200 in this Workbook.

Explore Tens

Name _____

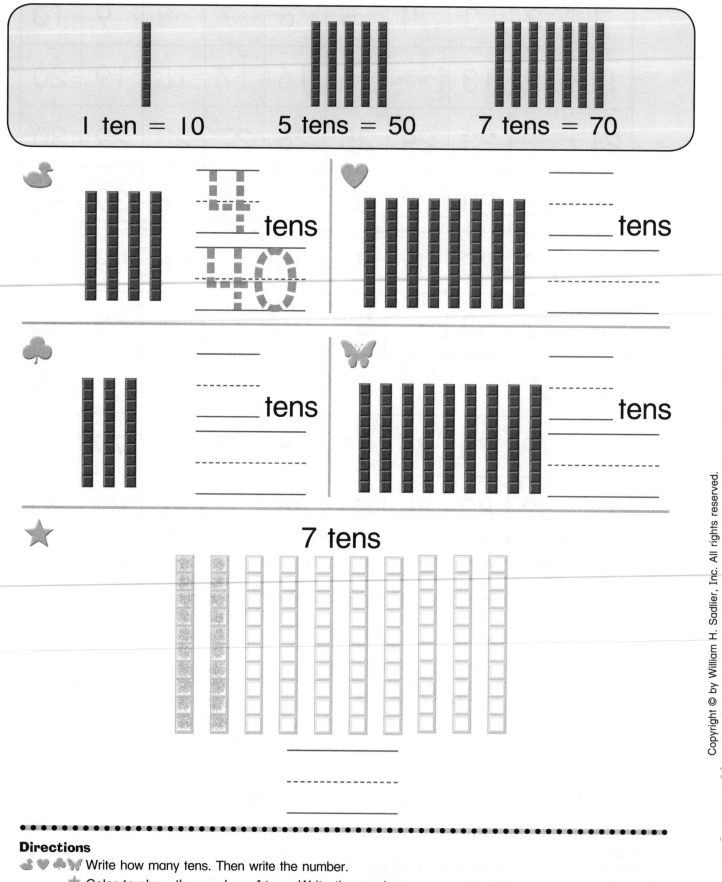

1 ten = 10   5 tens = 50   7 tens = 70

____ tens

____ tens

____ tens

____ tens

7 tens

____

____

Write how many tens. Then write the number.

Color to show the number of tens. Write the number.

134

Use with Lesson 12-2, pages 407–408 in the Student Book.
Then go to Lesson 12-3, pages 409–410 in the Student Book.

Explore Tens and Ones

Name _____

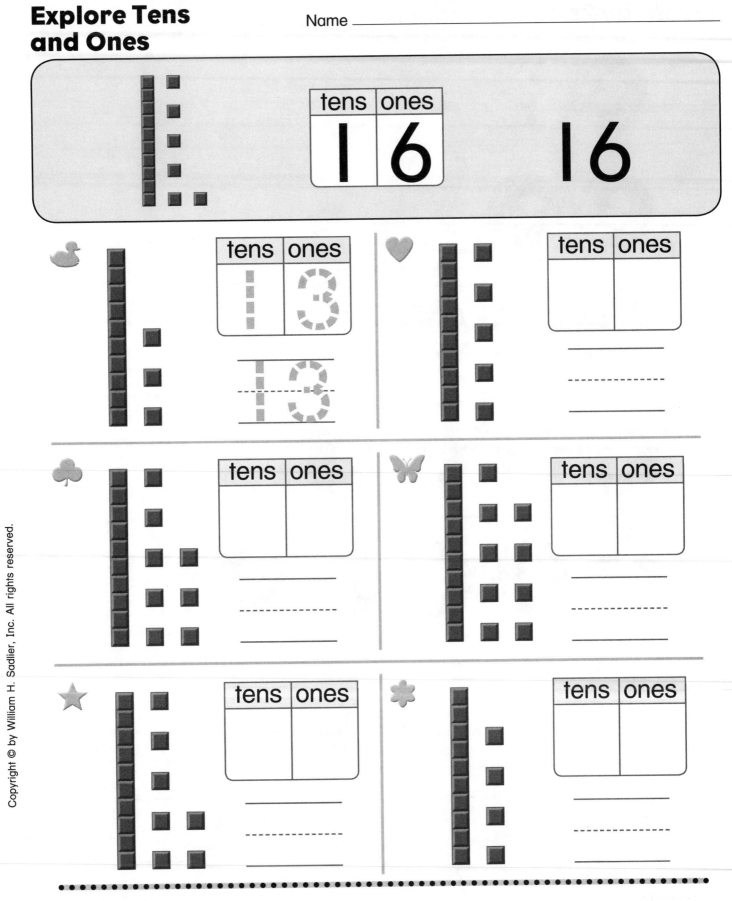

tens	ones
1	6

16

🦆
tens	ones
1	3

♥
tens	ones

♣
tens	ones

🦋
tens	ones

★
tens	ones

❀
tens	ones

Directions
🦆♥♣🦋★❀ Write how many tens and ones.
Then write the number.

C Use with Lesson 12-3, pages 409–410 in the Student Book.
C Then go to Lesson 12-3A, pages 201–202 in this Workbook.

135

Count by 2s

Name _____

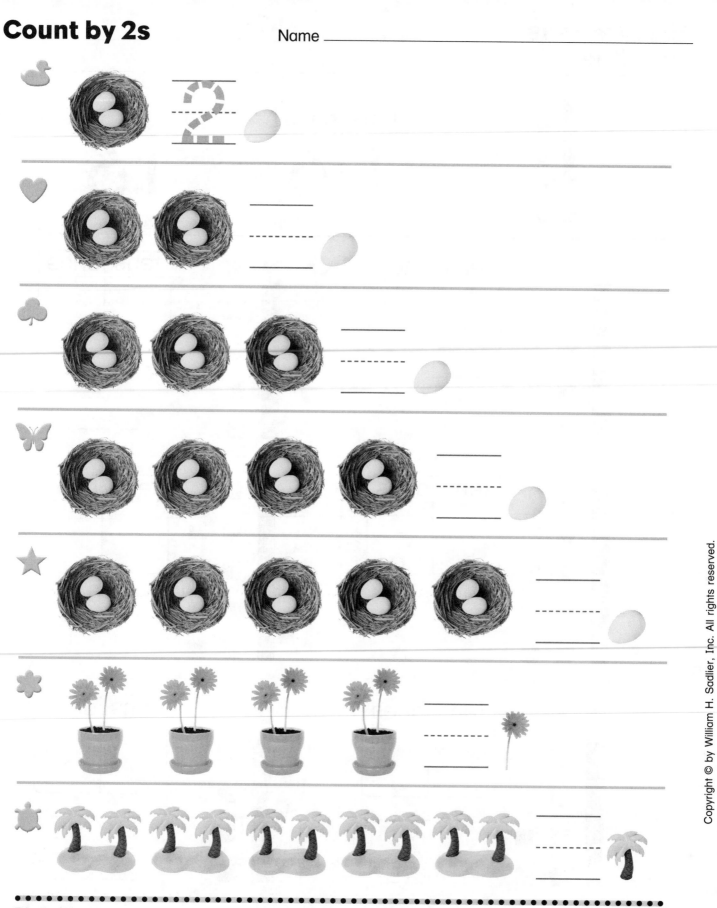

Directions

Count the objects by 2s.
Write the number in all.

136

Count by 5s

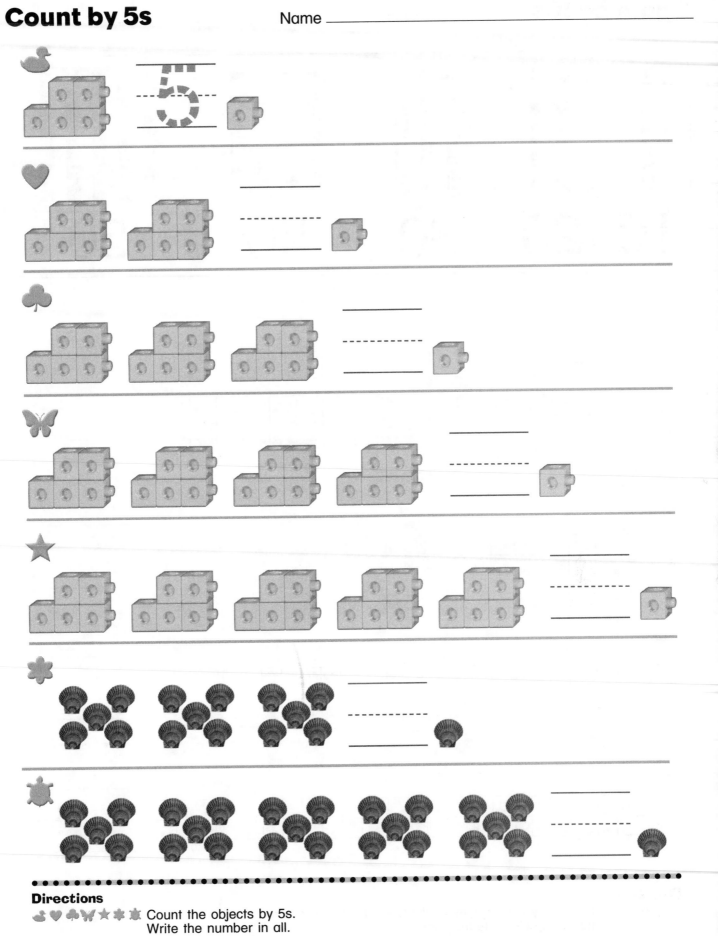

5

Directions

Count the objects by 5s.
Write the number in all.

Use with Lesson 12-5, pages 415–416 in the Student Book.
Then go to Lesson 12-6, pages 417–418 in the Student Book.

Count by 10s

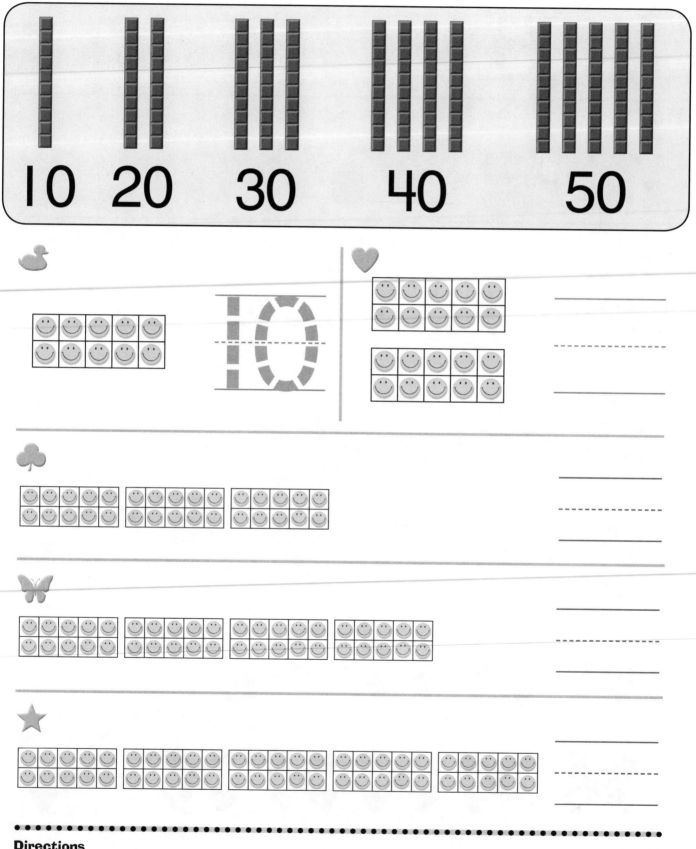

10   20   30   40   50

• •

Directions

🦆 ♥ ♣ 🦋 ★ How many smiley faces in all? Count by 10s to find the
number in all. Write the number.

138

Odd or Even

Name _____

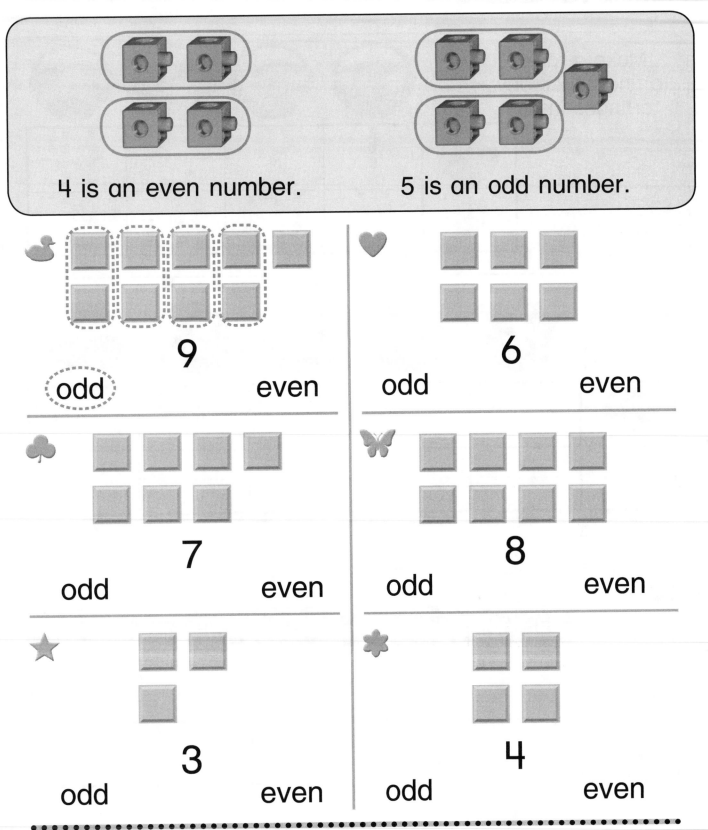

4 is an even number.

5 is an odd number.

🦆 9 (odd)   even

❤️ 6   odd   even

♣️ 7   odd   even

🦋 8   odd   even

⭐ 3   odd   even

🌸 4   odd   even

Directions

🦆❤️♣️🦋⭐🌸 Count the number of tiles. Circle pairs.
Then circle *odd* or *even*.

Use with Lesson 12-7, pages 419–420 in the Student Book.
Then go to Lesson 12-8, pages 421–422 in the Student Book.

139

Problem-Solving Strategy: Make a Table

Name _____

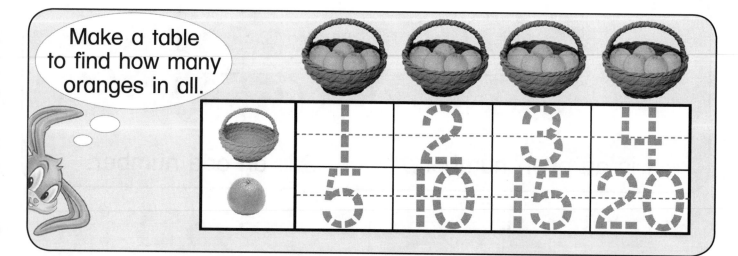

Make a table to find how many oranges in all.

🧺	1	2	3	4
🍊	5	10	15	20

🪺					
🥚					

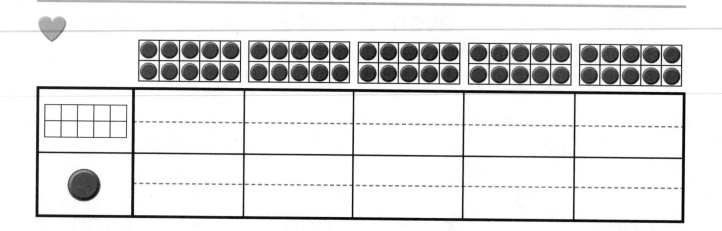

⊞					
●					

Directions
🦆 Make a table to find how many eggs in all. Circle the number in all.

♥ Make a table to find how many counters in all. Circle the number in all.

140

Use with Lesson 12-8, pages 421–422 in the Student Book.

Additional CCSS Lessons

Pages 143–202 of this workbook have additional lessons with content based on the Common Core State Standards (CCSS). Each lesson has teaching and practice exercises. These lessons can also be found online at progressinmathematics.com. The bottom of the second page of every lesson directs you to another workbook page of more practice of the math taught in the lesson and also to the next *Progress in Mathematics* lesson.

Practice for Additional CCSS Lessons

Pages 204–233 have more practice of the math taught in the additional CCSS lessons. Doing these practice exercises will help you master the work of each additional CCSS lesson more quickly. The bottom of every practice page identifies the lesson that is being reviewed by the workbook exercises, and also identifies the next *Progress in Mathematics* lesson. Before starting a workbook page, read the title. If you need to review the work in that lesson, turn to the page in your workbook where it is taught.

Additional CCSS Lessons

Name _____

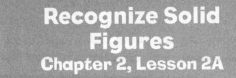

Objective: To identify solid figures in the environment

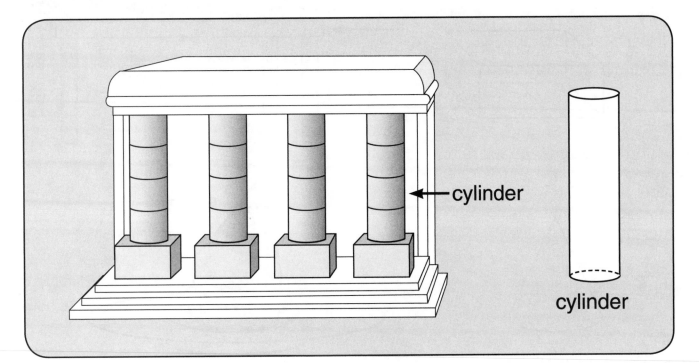

←— cylinder

cylinder

· ·

Directions

🦆 Color all the spheres.

💜 Color all the cones.

Talk It Over

Name some things in the real world that are shaped like a sphere.

Name _____

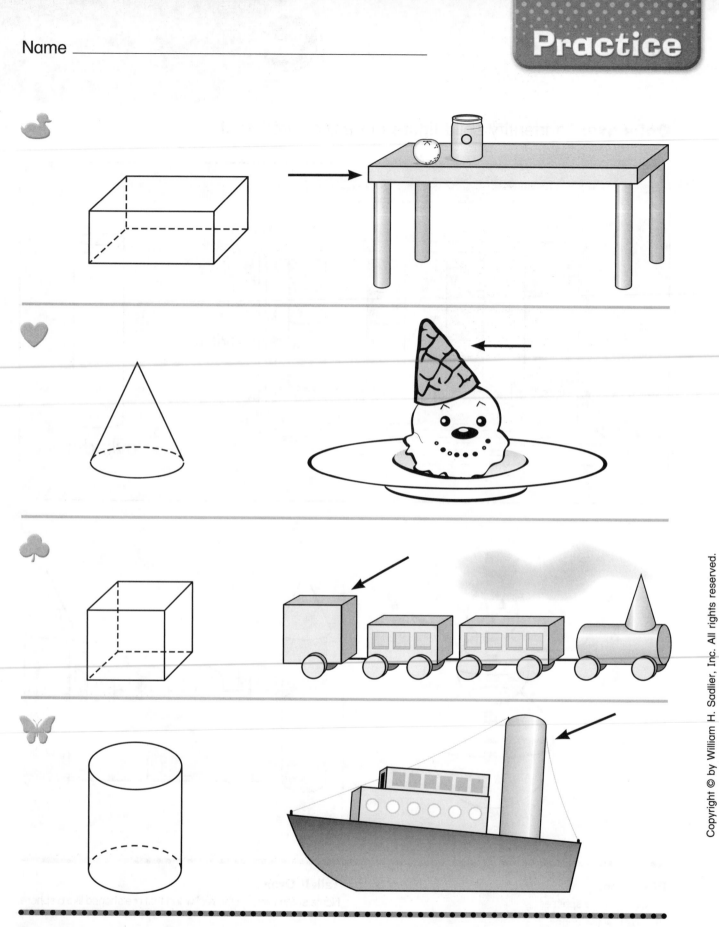

Directions

🦆 Trace the solid figure. Say the shape of the table top.

♥ Trace the solid figure. Say the shape of the clown's hat.

♣ Trace the solid figure. Say the shape of the caboose.

🦋 Trace the solid figure. Say the shape of the smoke stack.

144 **Grade K, Lesson 2-2A**

C For additional Practice, go to page 204 in this Workbook.
C Then go to Lesson 2-3, pages 41–42 in the Student Book.

Name _____

Objective: To describe similarities, differences, parts, and attributes of closed plane figures

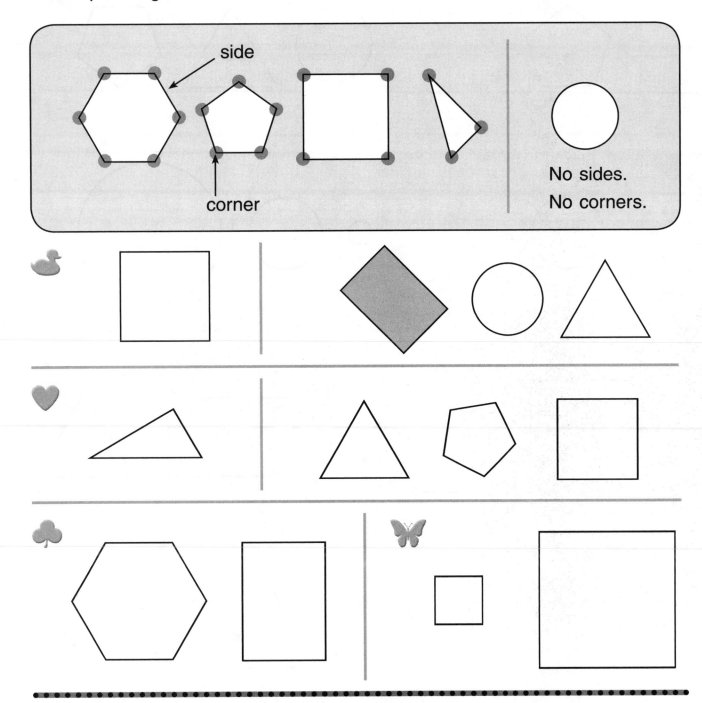

side

corner

No sides.
No corners.

Directions

🦆 Color the shape that has the same number of corners as the shape at the beginning of the row.

💜 Color the shape that has the same number of sides as the shape at the beginning of the row.

♣ Color the shape that has more sides.

🦋 Color the shape that is bigger.

Talk It Over

How are a square and a rectangle the same?
How are they different?

Name _____

Practice

Test Preparation

Directions

🦆 Color the shape that has the same number of corners as the shape at the beginning of the row.

💜 Color the shape that is the same size as the shape at the beginning of the row.

♣ Color the shape that has more sides.

🦋 Color the shape that has more corners.

Test Preparation

⭐ Which shape does not have any corners? *Fill in the circle under the correct answer.*

 **Grade K, Lesson 2-4A**

C For additional Practice, go to page 205 in this Workbook.

C Then go to Lesson 2-5, pages 45–46 in the Student Book.

Name _____

Objective: To compare parts and attributes of plane and solid figures in different sizes and orientations

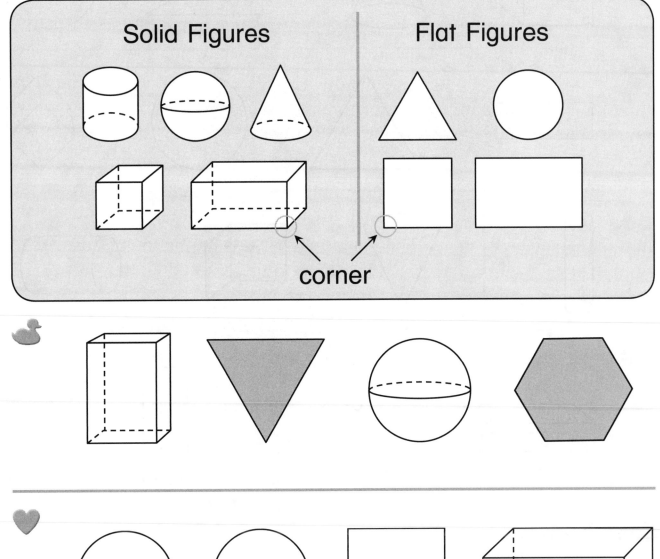

Solid Figures | Flat Figures

corner

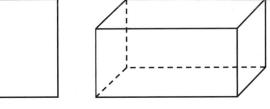

Directions
🦆 Color the shapes that are flat.
💜 Color the shapes that have corners.

Talk It Over
How are a circle and a sphere the same?
How are they different?

Name _____

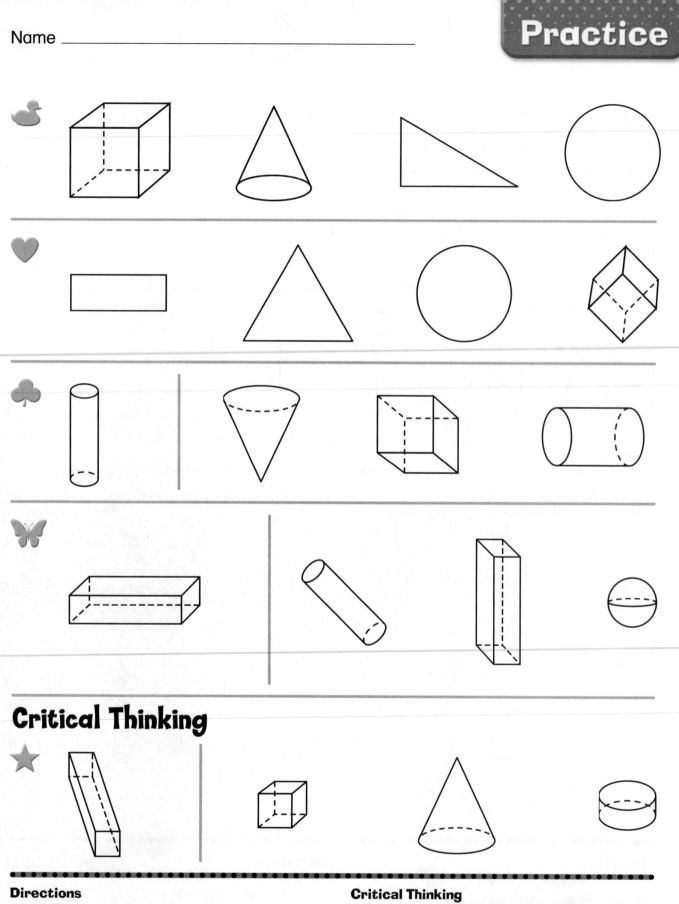

Critical Thinking

- -

Directions

🦆 Color the shapes that are solid.

💜 Color the shapes that have corners.

♣ 🦋 Circle the shape that is the same type of shape as
the shape at the beginning of the row.

Critical Thinking

⭐ Circle the shape with the same number of corners as the
shape at the beginning of the row.

148 **Grade K, Lesson 2-7A**

 For additional Practice, go to page 206 in this Workbook.
 Then go to Lesson 2-8, pages 51–52 in the Student Book.

Objective: To use the terms *inside*, *outside*, and *beside* to describe one shape in relation to another

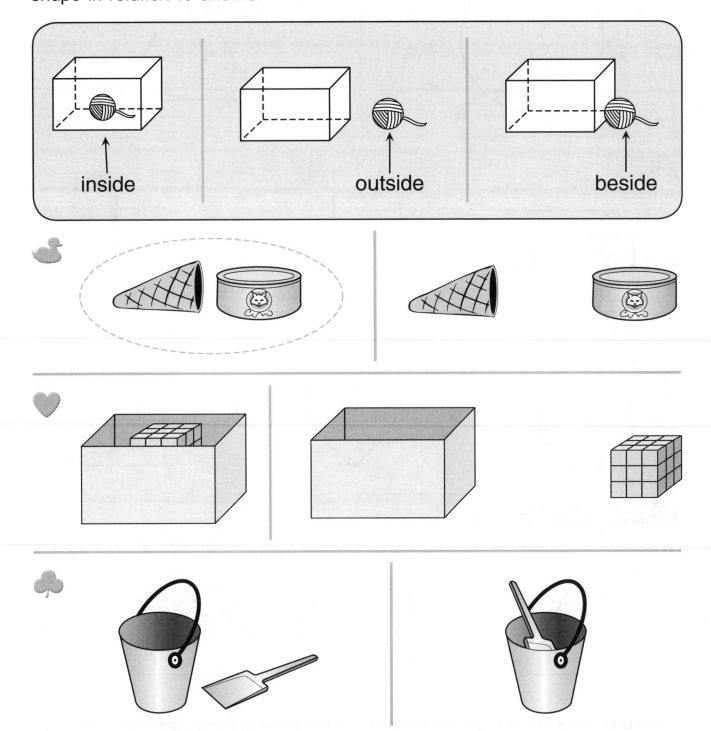

inside   outside   beside

Directions

🦆 Circle the picture that shows the cone beside the cylinder.
💜 Circle the picture that shows the cube outside the box.
♣ Circle the picture that shows the shovel inside the pail.

Talk It Over

What is the difference between being outside of a box and being beside a box?

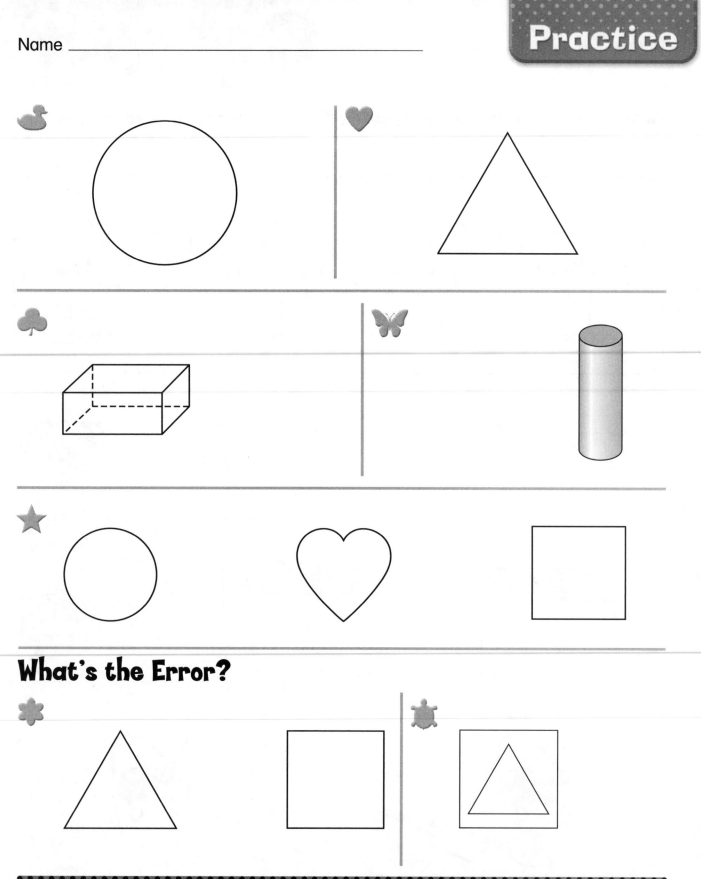

Name _____

What's the Error?

Directions

🦆💜 Name the shape. Then draw a rectangle inside the shape.

♣🦋 Name the shape. Then draw a circle beside the shape.

⭐ Draw a triangle beside the square.

What's the Error?

❀ David drew this picture to show a triangle inside a square. What error did David make?

🐢 Jenny drew this picture to show a square inside a triangle. What error did Jenny make?

☾ For additional Practice, go to page 207 in this Workbook.
☾ Then go to Lesson 3-5, pages 87–88 in the Student Book.

150 Grade K, Lesson 3-4A

Name _____

Objective: To use the terms *in front*, *behind*, and *next to*, to describe one object in relation to another

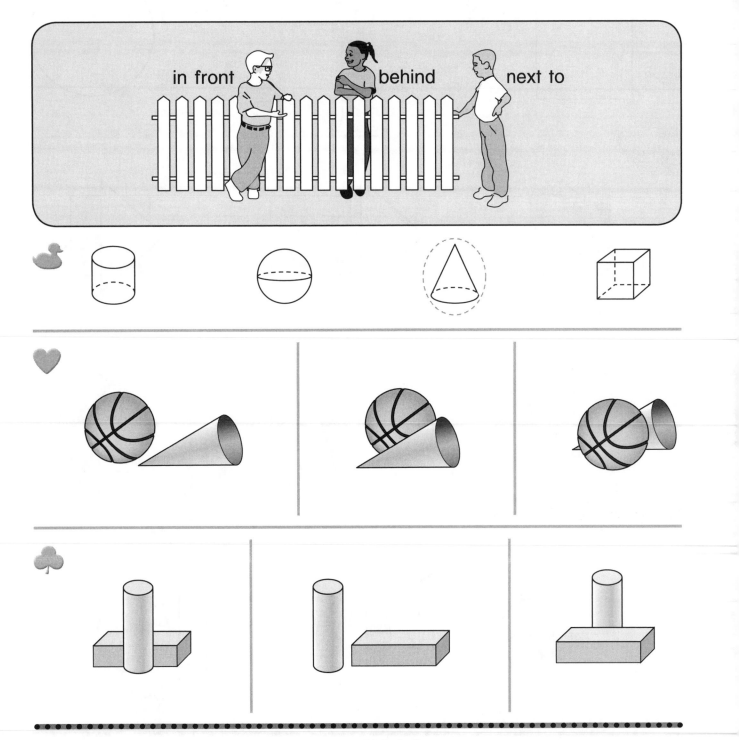

in front   behind   next to

Directions

🦆 Circle the object that is next to the cube.

💜 Circle the picture that shows the sphere behind a cone.

♣ Circle the picture that shows the rectangular prism in front of a cylinder.

Talk It Over

Look at the 💜 exercise. Where is the sphere in the first picture? Where is the sphere in the last picture?

Name _____

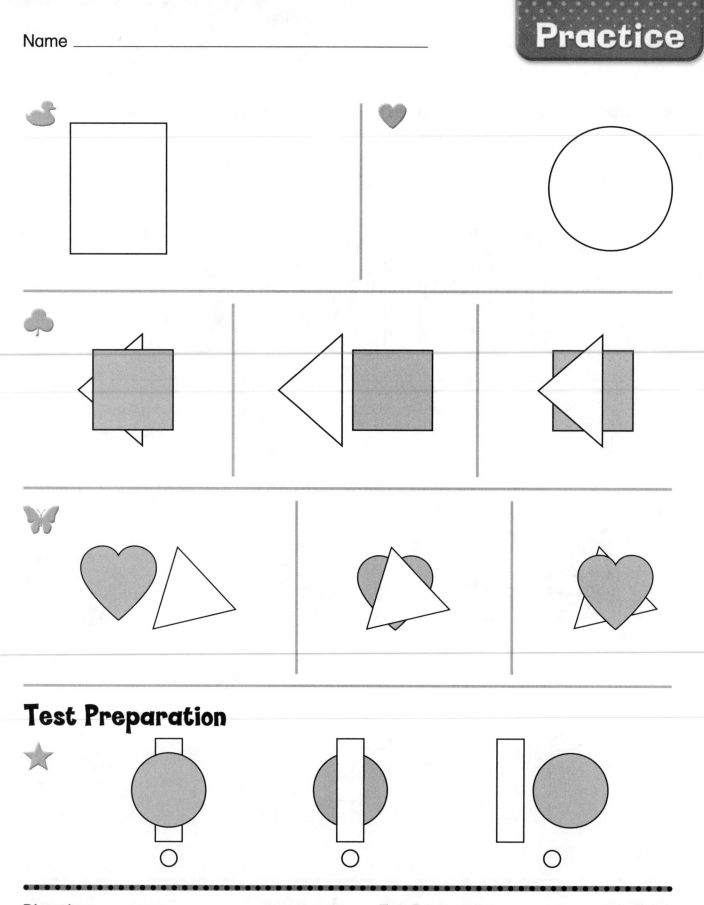

Test Preparation

Directions

🦆 ❤️ Name the shape. Then draw a triangle next to the shape.

♣ Circle the picture that shows the square behind a triangle.

🦋 Circle the picture that shows the heart next to a triangle.

Test Preparation

⭐ Which shows a rectangle next to a circle? *Fill in the circle under the correct answer.*

☾ For additional Practice, go to page 208 in this Workbook.

☾ Then go to Lesson 3-6, pages 89–90 in the Student Book.

Name _____

Objective: To count the number of objects in a group of up to five objects and tell how many

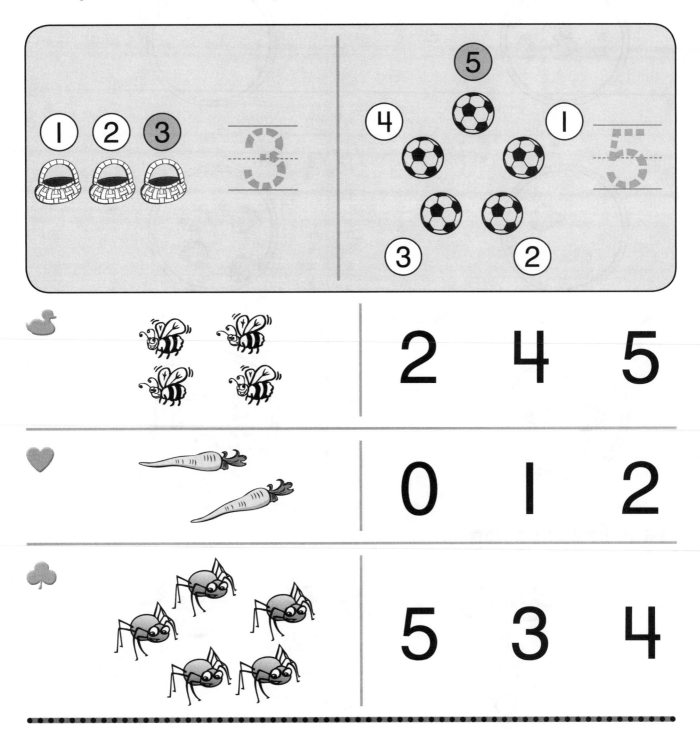

Directions

🦆 Count the bees. Circle the number that tells how many.

💜 Count the carrots. Circle the number that tells how many.

♣ Count the spiders. Circle the number that tells how many.

Talk It Over

Explain how counting helps you tell how many objects are in a group.

Name _____

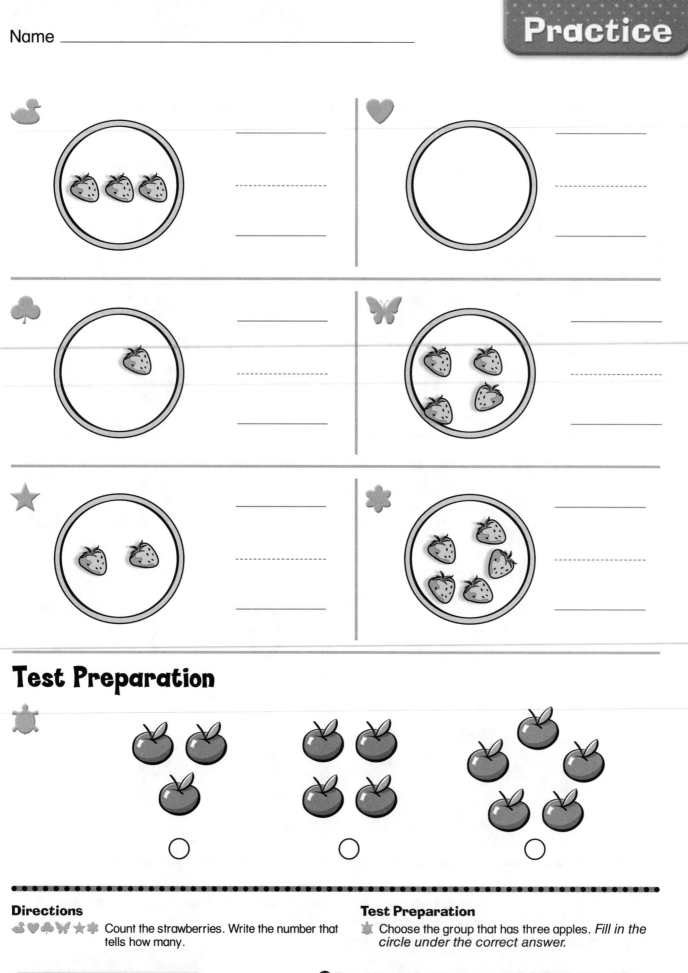

Test Preparation

Directions

🦆♥️♣️🦋⭐🍀 Count the strawberries. Write the number that tells how many.

Test Preparation

🐢 Choose the group that has three apples. *Fill in the circle under the correct answer.*

C For additional Practice, go to page 209 in this Workbook.
C Then go to Lesson 4-8B, pages 155–156 in this Workbook.

Name _____

Objective: To order numbers from 0–5; to count from any number to 5

0 1 2 3 4 5

1

2

3

Directions

🦆 Start at 1. Count to 5. Write the numbers in order.

💜 Start at 2. Count to 5. Write the numbers in order.

♣ Start at 3. Count to 5. Write the numbers in order.

Talk It Over

What number is one more than 3?
How do you know?

Critical Thinking

| 1 | 5 | 2 | 3 | 0 | 4 | 2 | 3 | 4 |

- -

Directions
🦆 Count how many in each group. Write the numbers.

💜 Write the numbers in the 🦆 exercise in number order.

♣ Count how many in each group. Write the numbers.

🦋 Write the numbers in the ♣ exercise in number order.

Critical Thinking
⭐ Circle the set of numbers that are in number order.

For additional Practice, go to page 210 in this Workbook.
Then go to Lesson 4-8C, pages 157–158 in this Workbook.

Name _____

Objective: To break apart groups with 2 to 5 objects into two parts in more than one way

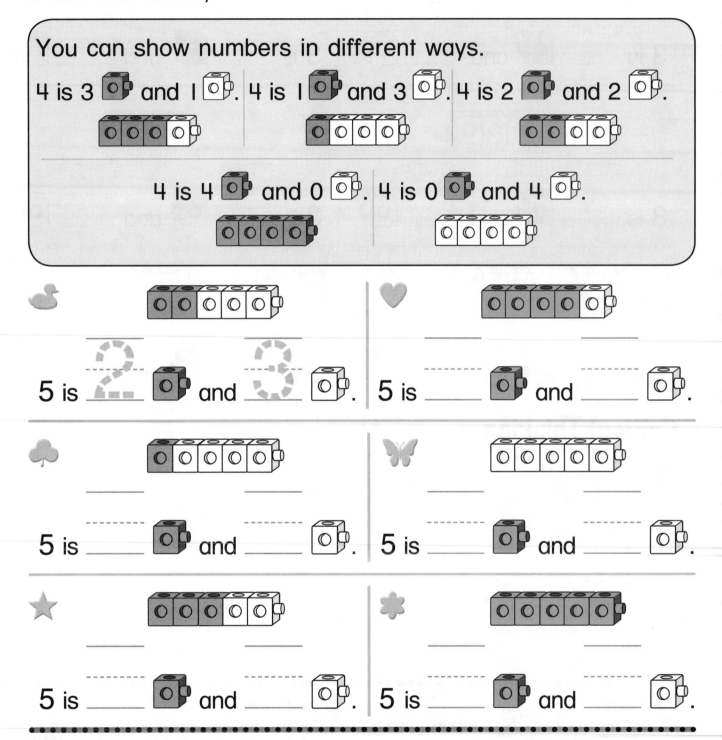

You can show numbers in different ways.

4 is 3 and 1. 4 is 1 and 3. 4 is 2 and 2.

4 is 4 and 0. 4 is 0 and 4.

5 is 2 and 3. 5 is ___ and ___.

5 is ___ and ___. 5 is ___ and ___.

5 is ___ and ___. 5 is ___ and ___.

Directions

Write numbers to show how to break apart 5 into two parts.

Talk It Over

How can you break apart a number into two smaller numbers?

Name _____

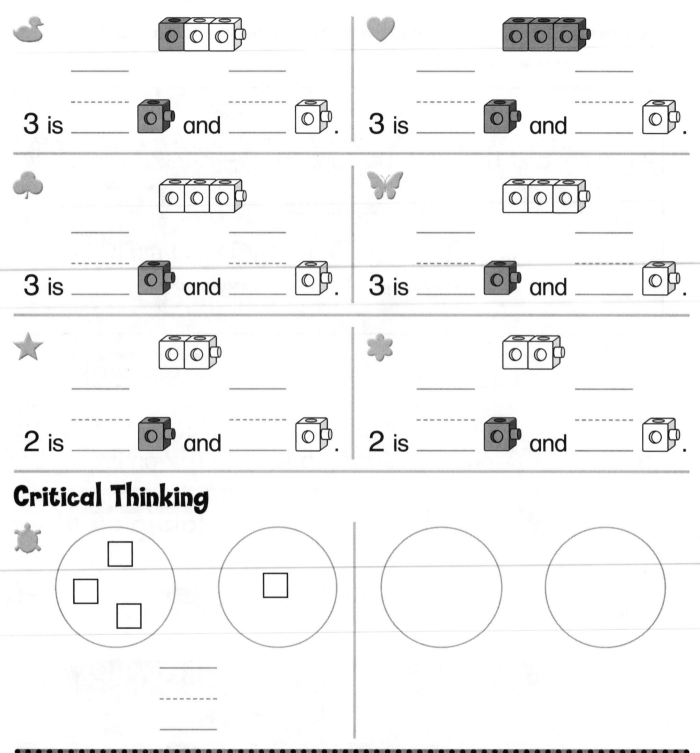

3 is _____ and _____ .

3 is _____ and _____ .

3 is _____ and _____ .

3 is _____ and _____ .

2 is _____ and _____ .

2 is _____ and _____ .

Critical Thinking

_____

Directions

🦆❤️ Write numbers to show how to break apart 3 into two parts.

♣️🦋 Color to show 3 in different ways. Write numbers to show the two parts.

⭐🌸 Color to show 2 in different ways. Write numbers to show the two parts.

Critical Thinking

🐢 Count the squares inside the circles. Write the number that tells how many. Then draw squares to show the number another way.

C For additional Practice, go to page 211 in this Workbook. Then go to Lesson 4-9, pages 129–130 in the Student Book.

Name _____

Objective: To decompose 6 and 7 into two parts or subgroups of objects

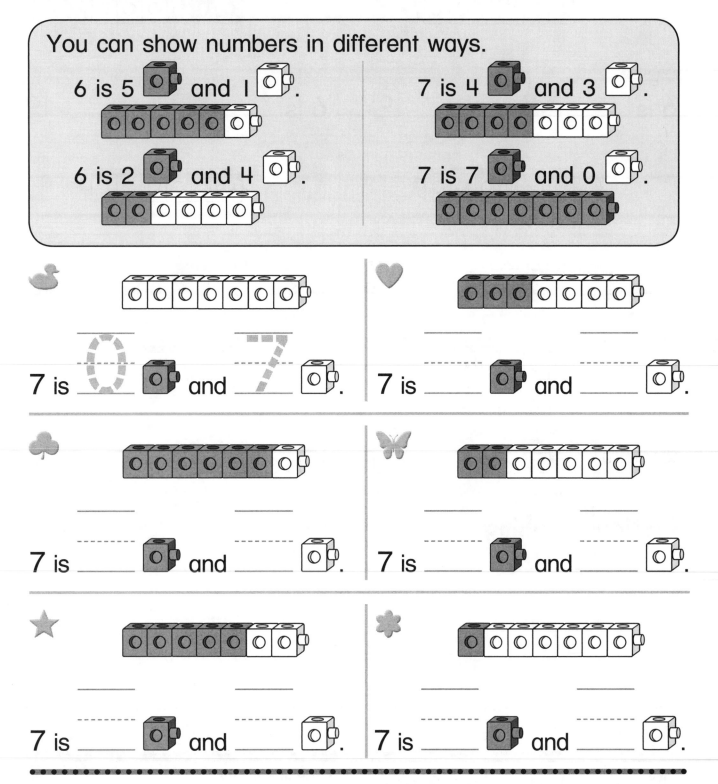

You can show numbers in different ways.

6 is 5 🟥 and 1 ⬜.

7 is 4 🟥 and 3 ⬜.

6 is 2 🟥 and 4 ⬜.

7 is 7 🟥 and 0 ⬜.

🦆 7 is ___0___ 🟥 and ___7___ ⬜.

❤️ 7 is _____ 🟥 and _____ ⬜.

♣️ 7 is _____ 🟥 and _____ ⬜.

🦋 7 is _____ 🟥 and _____ ⬜.

⭐ 7 is _____ 🟥 and _____ ⬜.

✳️ 7 is _____ 🟥 and _____ ⬜.

Directions

🦆❤️♣️🦋⭐✳️ Write numbers to show how to break apart 7 into two parts.

Talk It Over

How many different ways can you show the number 7? Explain.

🦆 ▢▢▢▢▢▢

_____   _____

6 is _____ ▣ and _____ ▢.

♥ ▢▢▢▢▢▢

_____   _____

6 is _____ ▣ and _____ ▢.

♣ ▢▢▢▢▢▢

_____   _____

6 is _____ ▣ and _____ ▢.

🦋 ▢▢▢▢▢▢

_____   _____

6 is _____ ▣ and _____ ▢.

★ ▢▢▢▢▢▢

_____   _____

6 is _____ ▣ and _____ ▢.

✿ ▢▢▢▢▢▢

_____   _____

6 is _____ ▣ and _____ ▢.

Critical Thinking

🐢

_____

Directions

🦆♥ Write numbers to show how to break apart 6 into two parts.

♣🦋★✿ Color to show 6 in different ways. Write numbers to show the two parts.

Critical Thinking

🐢 Count the squares inside the circles. Write the number that tells how many. Then draw squares to show the number another way.

C For additional Practice, go to page 212 in this Workbook.
C Then go to Lesson 4-11, pages 135–136 in the Student Book.

Objective: To decompose 8 and 9 into two parts or subgroups of objects

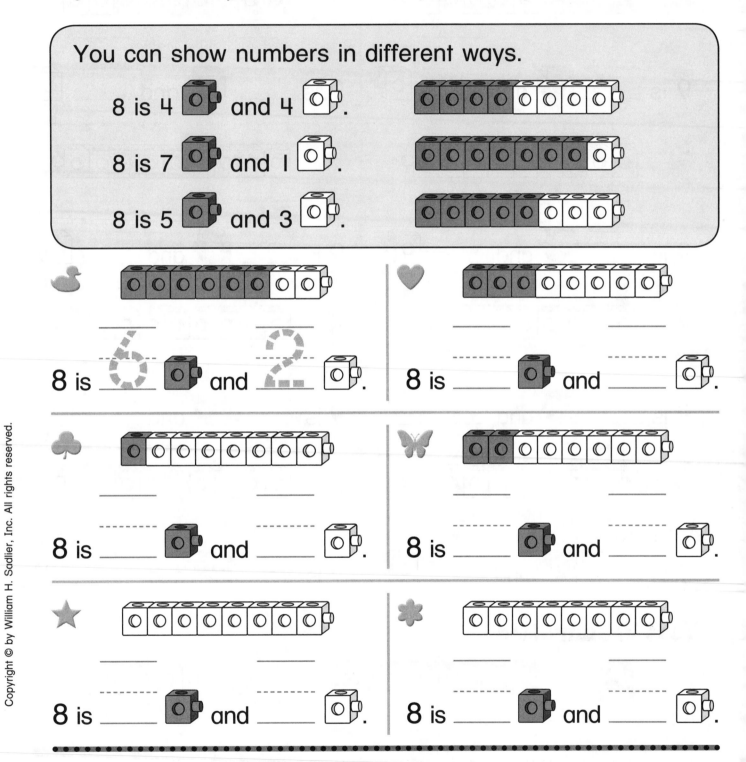

You can show numbers in different ways.

8 is 4 and 4 .

8 is 7 and 1 .

8 is 5 and 3 .

🦆 8 is 6 and 2 .

♥ 8 is ___ and ___ .

♣ 8 is ___ and ___ .

🦋 8 is ___ and ___ .

★ 8 is ___ and ___ .

✿ 8 is ___ and ___ .

Directions

🦆♥♣🦋 Write numbers to show how to break apart 8 into two parts.

★✿ Color to show 8 in different ways. Write numbers to show the two parts.

Talk It Over

Can you break apart 8 into two equal parts? Explain.

Name_____

🦆 ▢▢▢▢▢▢▢▢▢

_____ _____

9 is _____ ▢ and _____ ▢.

❤ ▢▢▢▢▢▢▢▢▢

_____ _____

9 is _____ ▢ and _____ ▢.

♣ ▢▢▢▢▢▢▢▢▢

_____ _____

9 is _____ ▢ and _____ ▢.

🦋 ▢▢▢▢▢▢▢▢▢

_____ _____

9 is _____ ▢ and _____ ▢.

★ ▢▢▢▢▢▢▢▢▢

_____ _____

9 is _____ ▢ and _____ ▢.

✿ ▢▢▢▢▢▢▢▢▢

_____ _____

9 is _____ ▢ and _____ ▢.

🐢 ▢▢▢▢▢▢▢▢▢

_____ _____

9 is _____ ▢ and _____ ▢.

🧸 ▢▢▢▢▢▢▢▢▢

_____ _____

9 is _____ ▢ and _____ ▢.

Test Preparation

🎵 **8** ▢▢▢▢▢▢▢▢ ▢▢▢▢▢▢▢

○ ○

Directions

🦆❤ Write numbers to show how to break apart 9 into two parts.

♣🦋★✿🐢🧸 Color to show 9 in different ways. Write numbers to show the two parts.

Test Preparation

🎵 Fill in the circle under the cubes that show a way to make 8.

162 **Grade K, Lesson 4-11A**

🅒 For additional Practice, go to page 213 in this Workbook.
🅒 Then go to Lesson 4-12, pages 137–138 in the Student Book.

Copyright © by William H. Sadlier, Inc. All rights reserved.

Name _____

Ways to Make 10
Chapter 4, Lesson 12A

Objective: To decompose 10 into two parts or subgroups of objects

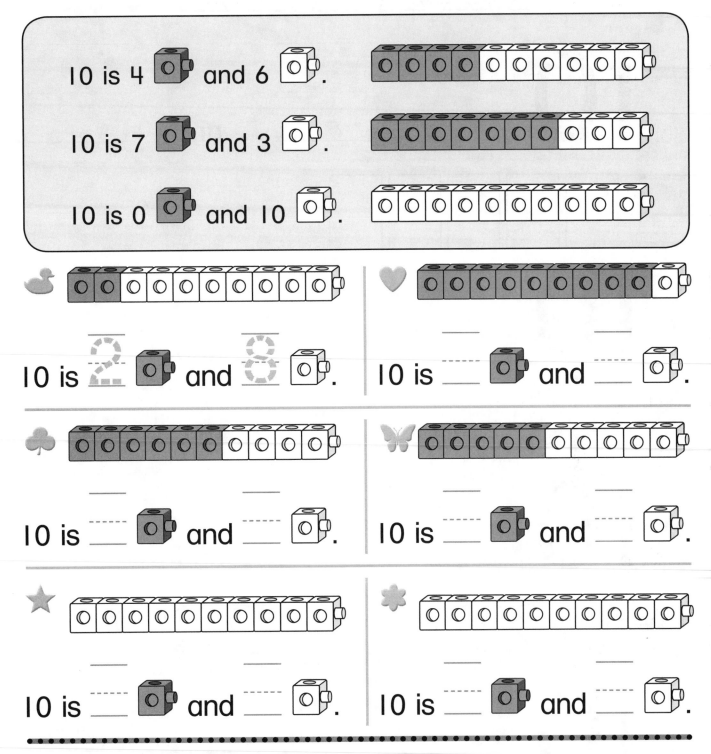

10 is 4 and 6.

10 is 7 and 3.

10 is 0 and 10.

🦆 10 is 2 and 8.

❤️ 10 is ___ and ___.

♣️ 10 is ___ and ___.

🦋 10 is ___ and ___.

⭐ 10 is ___ and ___.

✳️ 10 is ___ and ___.

Directions

🦆❤️♣️🦋 Write numbers to show how to break apart 10 into two parts.

⭐✳️ Color to show 10 in different ways. Write numbers to show the two parts.

Talk It Over

How can you find two numbers that make 10?

Name _____

🦆 △ △ △ △ △ △ △ △ △ △

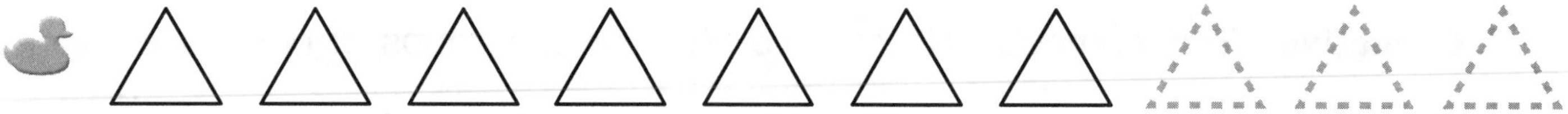

10 is 7 and 3 .

♥ ☐ ☐ ☐ ☐ ☐

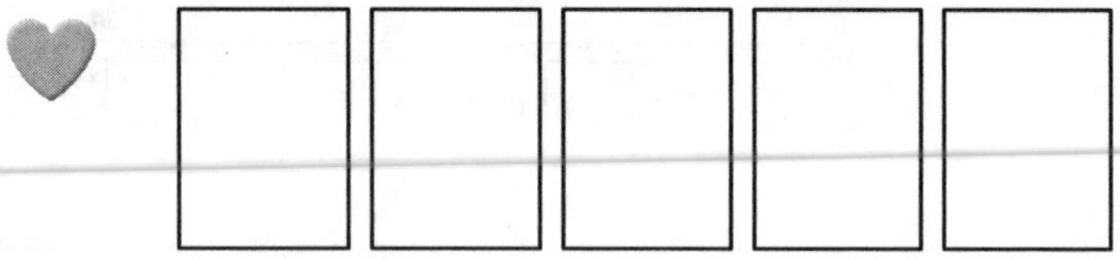

10 is _____ and _____ .

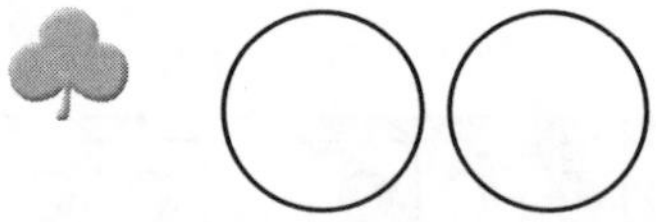

♣ ○ ○

10 is _____ and _____ .

🦋 ♡ ♡ ♡ ♡ ♡ ♡ ♡ ♡ ♡

10 is _____ and _____ .

Directions

🦆♥♣🦋 Draw more of the same shapes to make 10. Write the number for each part.

C For additional Practice, go to page 214 in this Workbook.
C Then go to Lesson 4-12B, pages 165–166 in this Workbook.

Objective: To identify the number that names the quantity that is one more or one fewer than a given quantity

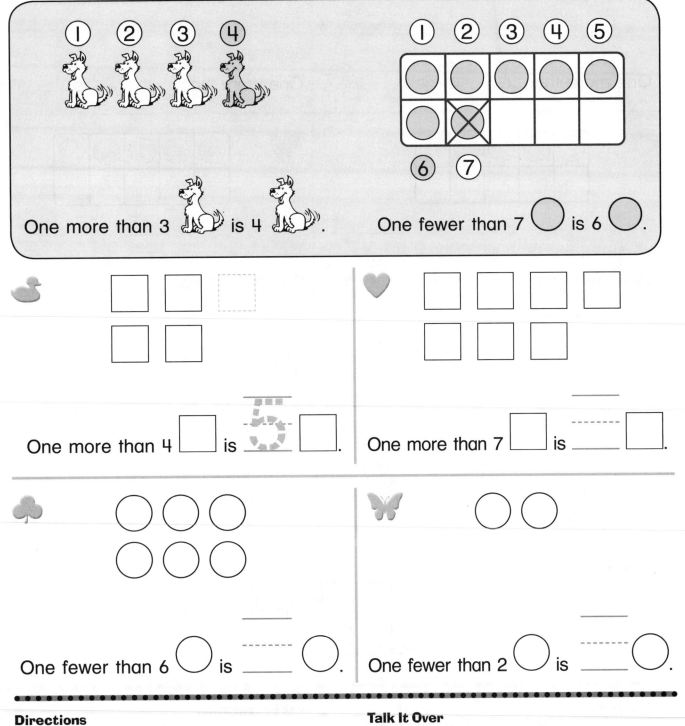

① ② ③ ④

One more than 3 🐕 is 4 🐕.

① ② ③ ④ ⑤

⑥ ⑦

One fewer than 7 ◯ is 6 ◯.

One more than 4 ☐ is 5 ☐.

One more than 7 ☐ is _____ ☐.

One fewer than 6 ◯ is _____ ◯.

One fewer than 2 ◯ is _____ ◯.

Directions

🦆 ♥ Count the squares. Draw one more. Write the number of squares that is one more.

♣ 🦋 Count the circles. Cross out one circle. Write the number of circles that is one fewer.

Talk It Over

What number is one fewer than nine?
How do you know?

Name _____

One more than _____ ◯ is _____ ◯.

One more than _____ ◯ is _____ ◯.

One fewer than _____ ◯ is _____ ◯.

One fewer than _____ ◯ is _____ ◯.

Test Preparation

Directions

🦆 💙 Count the counters. Draw one more. Write the numbers.

♣ 🦋 Count the counters. Cross out one. Write the numbers.

⭐ Count the objects. Draw one more. Write the number.

✿ Count the objects. Cross out one. Write the number.

Test Preparation

🐢 Draw one more counter. Then write the number.

C For additional Practice, go to page 215 in this Workbook.
C Then go to Lesson 4-12C, pages 167–168 in this Workbook.

Name _____

Objective: To compare the number of objects in a group from 0 to 10 using counting strategies

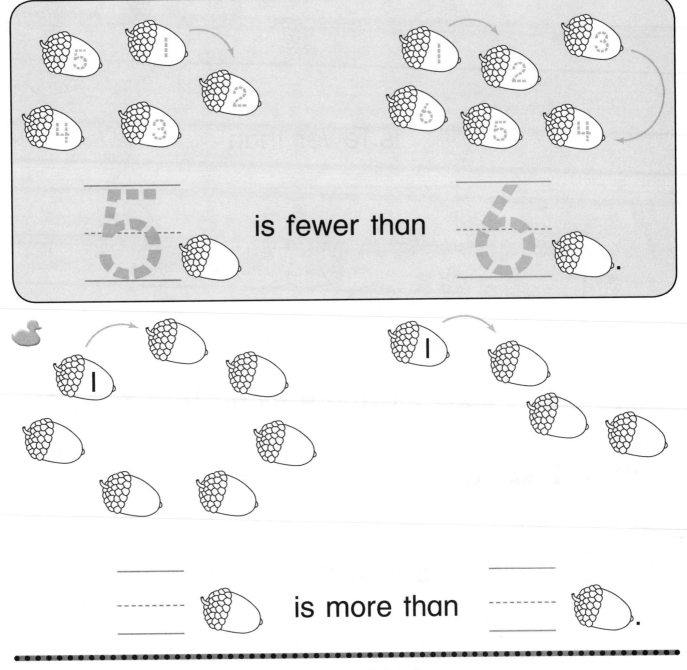

is fewer than

is more than

Directions

Count the acorns on the left. Write the number in each acorn as you count. Then write how many below. Now count the acorns on the right. Write the number in each acorn as you count. Then write how many below. Tell which number is more.

Talk It Over

How does counting help tell which number is greater?

Name _____

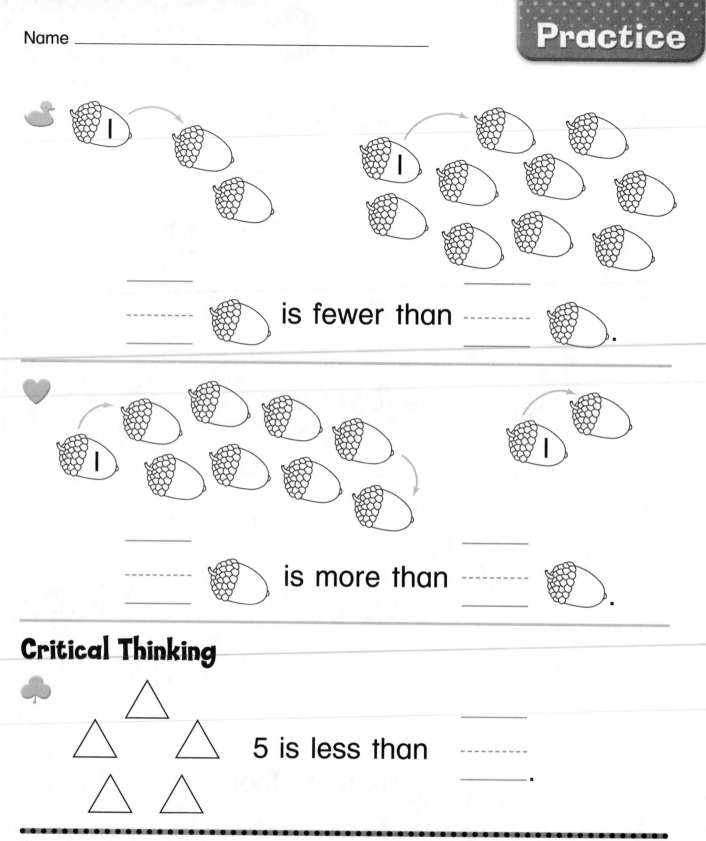

_____ is fewer than _____ 🌰.

_____ is more than _____ 🌰.

Critical Thinking

5 is less than _____

Directions

🦆 Count the acorns on the left. Write the number in each acorn as you count. Then write how many below. Now count the acorns on the right. Write the number in each acorn as you count. Then write how many below. Tell which number is fewer.

💜 Count the acorns on the left. Write the number in each acorn as you count. Then write how many below. Now count the acorns on the right. Write the number in each acorn as you count. Then write how many below. Tell which number is more.

Critical Thinking

♣ Write a number to make the sentence true.

C For additional Practice, go to page 216 in this Workbook.
C Then go to Lessons 4-13 and 4-14, pages 139–142 in the Student Book.

Name _____

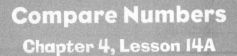

Compare Numbers
Chapter 4, Lesson 14A

Objective: To compare two numbers between 1 and 10 using a number line model

☆1 ☆2 ☆3 ☆4 ☆5 ☆6 ☆7 ☆8 ☆9 ☆10

7 is greater than 4.

☆1 ☆2 ☆3 ☆4 ☆5 ☆6 ☆7 ☆8 ☆9 ☆10

6 is less than 9.

🦆 ⬡1 ⬡2 ⬡3 ⬡4 ⬡5 ⬡6 ⬡7 ⬡8 ⬡9 ⬡10

2   ⟨6⟩

♥ 🏮1 🏮2 🏮3 🏮4 🏮5 🏮6 🏮7 🏮8 🏮9 🏮10

5   8

♣ △1 △2 △3 △4 △5 △6 △7 △8 △9 △10

3   9

Directions

🦆♥ Look at the number line. Circle the number that is greater.

♣ Look at the number line. Circle the number that is less.

Talk It Over

How do you compare two numbers to find which is greater?

Name _____

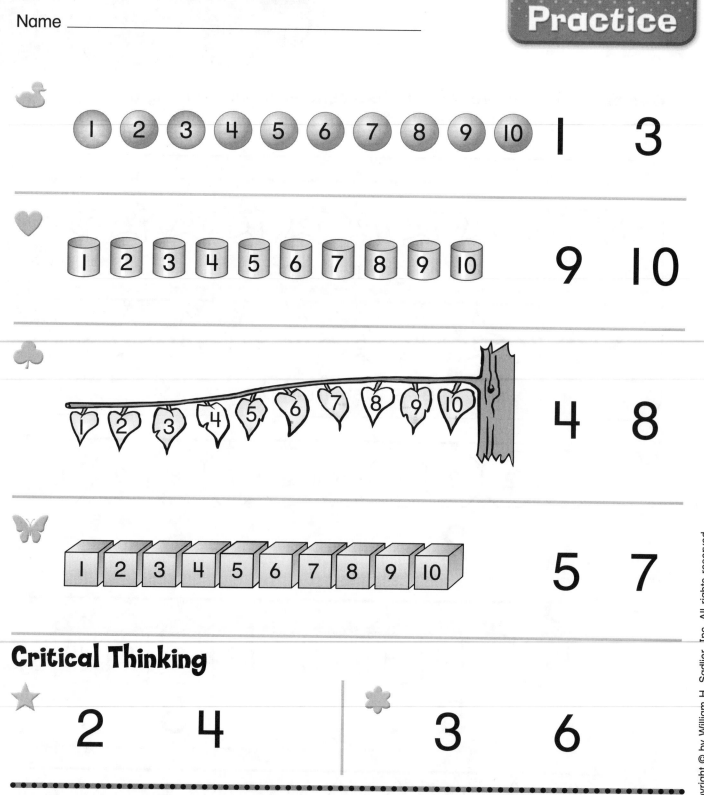

🦆 ① ② ③ ④ ⑤ ⑥ ⑦ ⑧ ⑨ ⑩   **1**   **3**

♥ 1 2 3 4 5 6 7 8 9 10   **9**   **10**

♣ 1 2 3 4 5 6 7 8 9 10   **4**   **8**

🦋 1 2 3 4 5 6 7 8 9 10   **5**   **7**

Critical Thinking

⭐   **2**   **4**   ❇   **3**   **6**

Directions

🦆 Color the balls with the numbers 1 and 3. Look at the numbers to the right. Circle the number that is greater.

♥ Color the cylinders with the numbers 9 and 10. Look at the numbers to the right. Circle the number that is less.

♣ Color the leaves with the numbers 4 and 8. Look at the numbers to the right. Circle the number that is less.

🦋 Color the cubes with the numbers 5 and 7. Look at the numbers to the right. Circle the number that is greater.

Critical Thinking

⭐ Circle the number that is greater. How do you know?

❇ Circle the number that is less. How do you know?

C For additional Practice, go to page 217 in this Workbook. Then go to Lesson 4-15, pages 143–144 in the Student Book.

Name _____

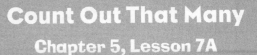

Count Out That Many
Chapter 5, Lesson 7A

Objective: To count out a given number of objects from 1–20

Directions

🍀♥ Use counters. Count out the number shown.
Then draw circles to show the number.
Write how many you drew.

Talk It Over

When you count out 9 objects, you say all the numbers from 1 to 9. Which number tells how many objects are in the group?

Name _____

🦆 14 _____

❤️ 16 _____

♣️ 20 _____

🦋 15 _____

Critical Thinking

⭐ 17

Directions

🦆❤️♣️🦋 Use counters. Count out the number shown. Draw circles to show the number. Write how many you drew.

Critical Thinking

⭐ Which shows 17? Circle the group.

🔵 For additional Practice, go to page 218 in this Workbook.
🔵 Then go to Lesson 5-7B, pages 173–174 in this Workbook.

Name _____

Objective: To count numbers through 20 starting from any number

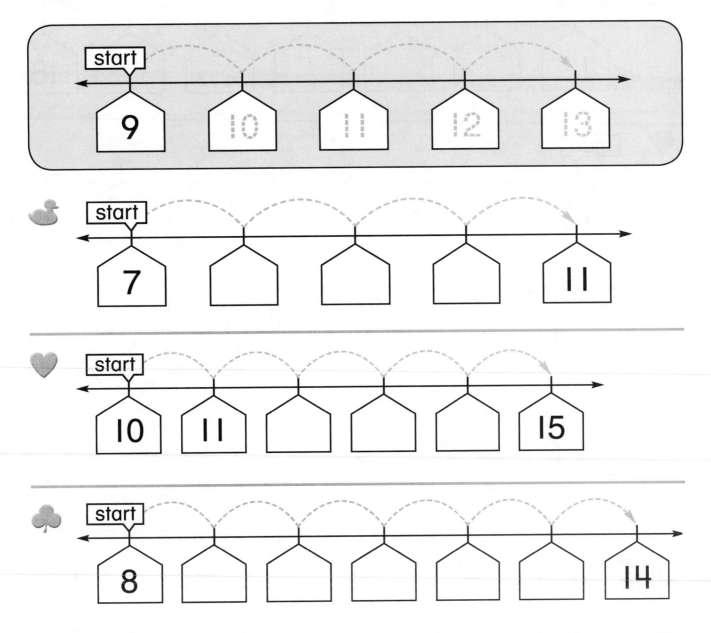

Directions

🦆 Count forward from 7 to 11. Write the numbers you count.

💜 Count forward from 10 to 15. Write the numbers you count.

♣ Count forward from 8 to 14. Write the numbers you count.

Talk It Over

Does the number 16 come before or after 17?　　How do you know?

Name _____

start 13 ... 20

What's the Error?

9, 10, 11, 12, 14, 13

Directions

🦆 Count forward from 12 to 18. Write the numbers you count.

💜 Count forward from 13 to 20. Write the numbers you count.

♣ Choose a number from 11 through 20. Write the number. Draw that many objects.

🦋 Count the moons. Write the number. How do you know that your answer is correct?

What's the Error?

⭐ Kim counted forward from 9. She wrote these numbers. What error did Kim make?

C For additional Practice, go to page 219 in this Workbook.
C Then go to Lesson 5-8, pages 175–176 in the Student Book.

174 Grade K, Lesson 5-7B

Practice

Copyright © by William H. Sadlier, Inc. All rights reserved.

Objective: To count objects in different categories

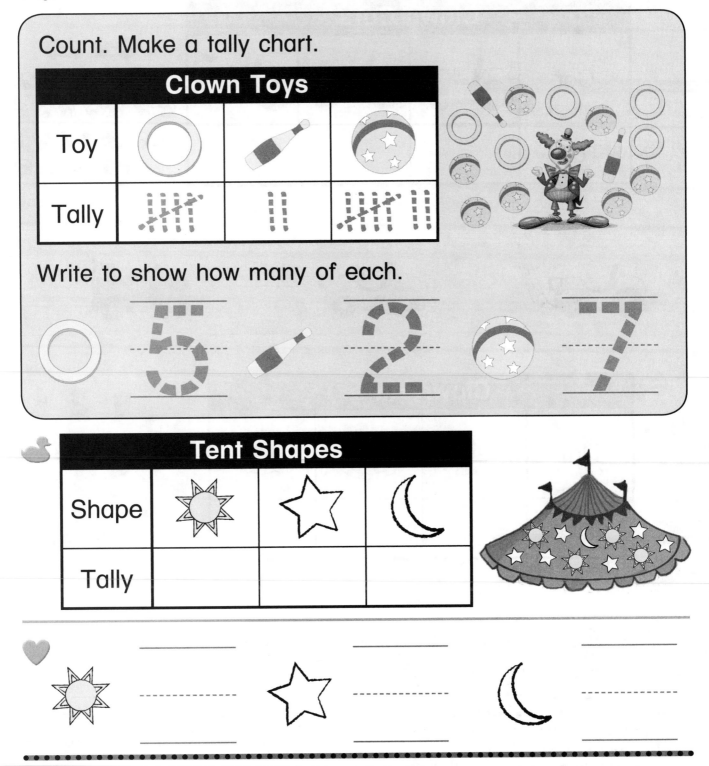

Count. Make a tally chart.

Clown Toys			
Toy	◯	🎳	🌙⭐
Tally	卌	𝐼𝐼	卌 𝐼𝐼

Write to show how many of each.

◯ 5   🎳 2   🌙 7

Tent Shapes			
Shape	☀	☆	🌙
Tally			

☀ _____   ☆ _____   🌙 _____

Directions

🦆 Count the tent shapes. Draw tally marks to show how many of each shape.

💜 Count the tally marks in the 🦆 exercise. Write the number next to each shape.

Talk It Over

Look at the number you wrote for each tent shape. Are there more stars than moons?   How do you know?

Name _____

Practice

Clown Cars

Car			
Tally			

Clown Hats

Hat			
Tally			

Directions

Count the clown cars. Draw tally marks to show how many of each car.

Count the tally marks in the 🚗 exercise. Write the number next to each car.

Count the clown hats. Draw tally marks to show how many of each hat.

Count the tally marks in the ♣ exercise. Write the number next to each hat.

Critical Thinking

Look at the 🦋 exercise. Circle the number that shows the most clown hats. Cross out the number that shows the fewest.

176 Grade K, Lesson 6-2A

For additional Practice, go to page 220 in this Workbook.
Then go to Lesson 6-3, pages 205–206 in the Student Book.

Name _____

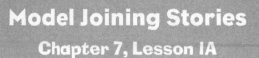
Objective: To model addition as the joining of two groups using concrete objects, stories, and actions

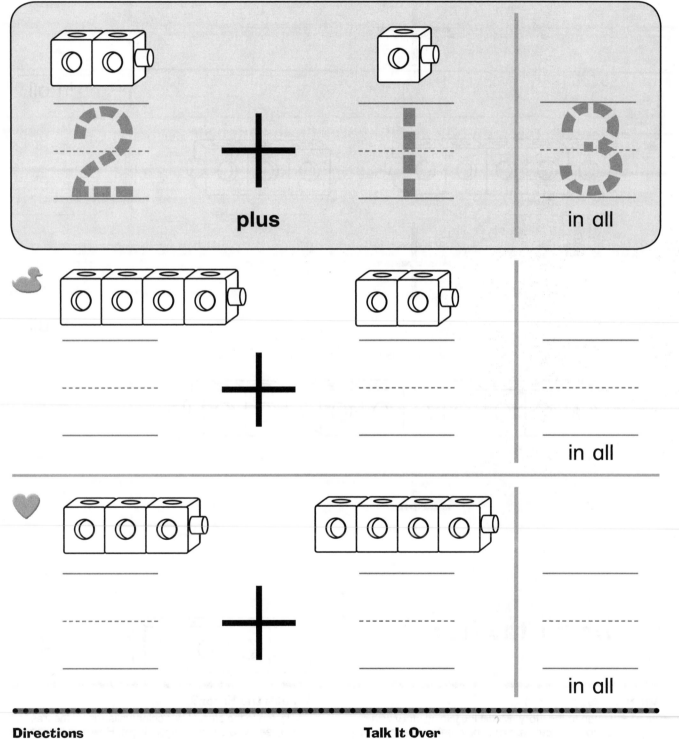

2 + 1 = 3

plus   in all

in all

in all

• •

Directions

Listen to the story. Model the joining story with connecting cubes. Write the number in each part. Then write how many in all.

Talk It Over

How do your models show joining stories?

Name _____

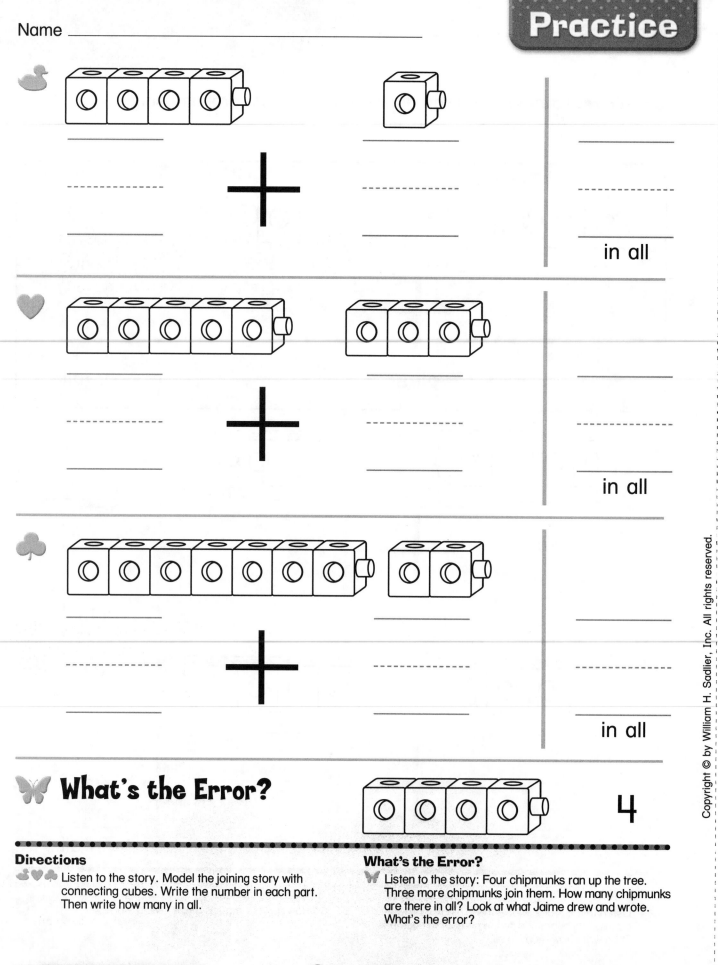

🦆

_____ + _____ = _____

in all

❤️

_____ + _____ = _____

in all

♣️

_____ + _____ = _____

in all

🦋 **What's the Error?**

4

Directions

🦆❤️♣️ Listen to the story. Model the joining story with connecting cubes. Write the number in each part. Then write how many in all.

What's the Error?

🦋 Listen to the story: Four chipmunks ran up the tree. Three more chipmunks join them. How many chipmunks are there in all? Look at what Jaime drew and wrote. What's the error?

📘 For additional Practice, go to page 221 in this Workbook.
📘 Then go to Lesson 7-2, pages 239–240 in the Student Book.

Objective: To use a bar model to add

Directions

🦆❤️ Listen to the story. Write the number in each part in the bar model. Then write a number sentence to show how many in all.

Talk It Over

How does the bar model help you find how many in all?

Name _____

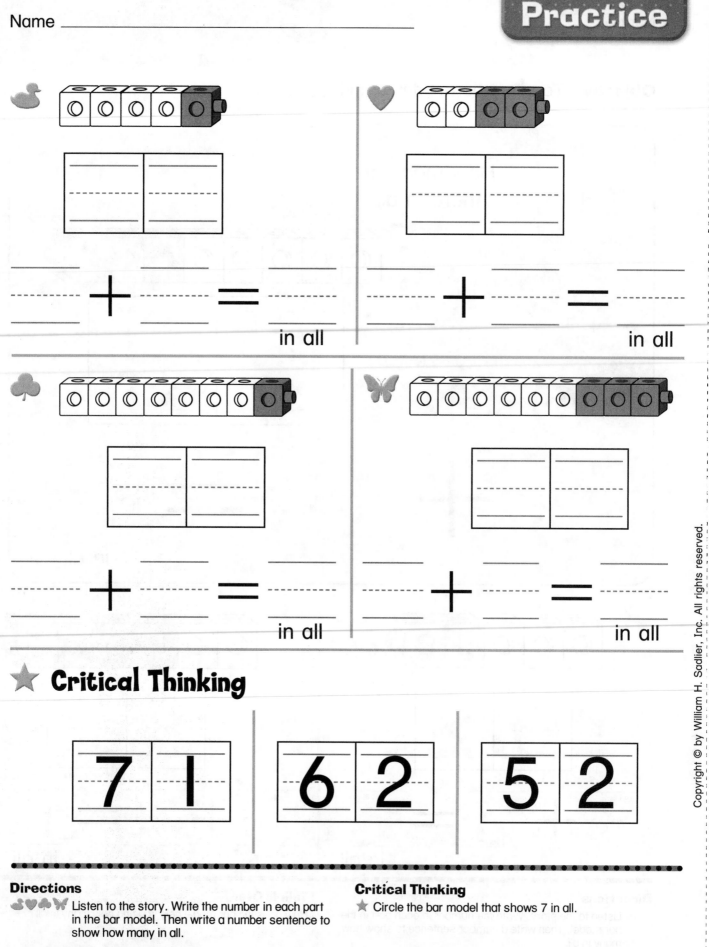

in all

in all

in all

in all

⭐ **Critical Thinking**

| 7 | l | | 6 | 2 | | 5 | 2 |

Directions

🦆💜♣🦋 Listen to the story. Write the number in each part in the bar model. Then write a number sentence to show how many in all.

Critical Thinking

⭐ Circle the bar model that shows 7 in all.

C For additional Practice, go to page 222 in this Workbook.
C Then go to Lesson 7-6, pages 249–250 in the Student Book.

Name _____

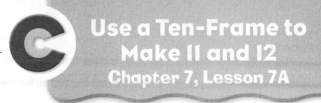

Objective: To understand 11 and 12 by reading, writing, counting, and using a ten-frame to model 11 and 12

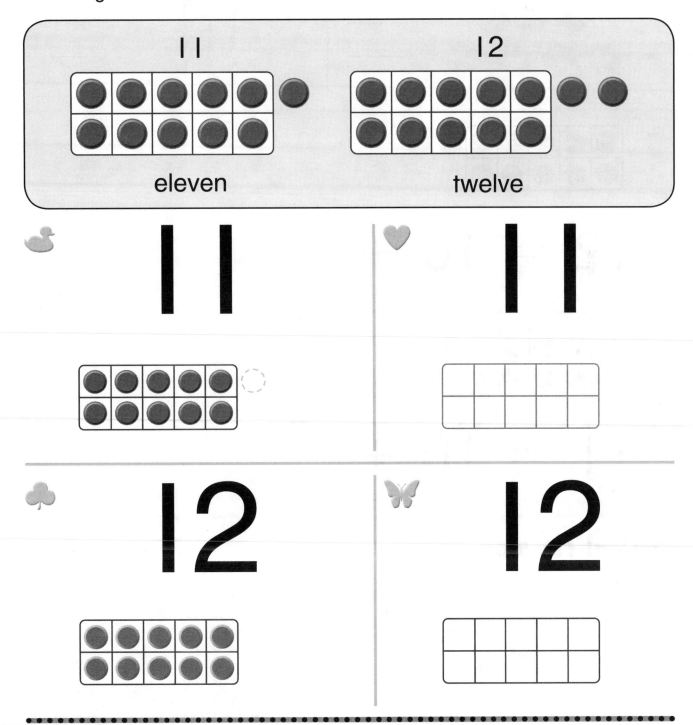

11

eleven

12

twelve

....

Directions

🦆❤️ Use the ten-frame. Draw more counters to show 11.

♣️🦋 Use the ten-frame. Draw more counters to show 12.

Talk It Over

Look at the top of the page. How many counters are in a full ten-frame?
Eleven is ten and how many more?
Twelve is ten and how many more?

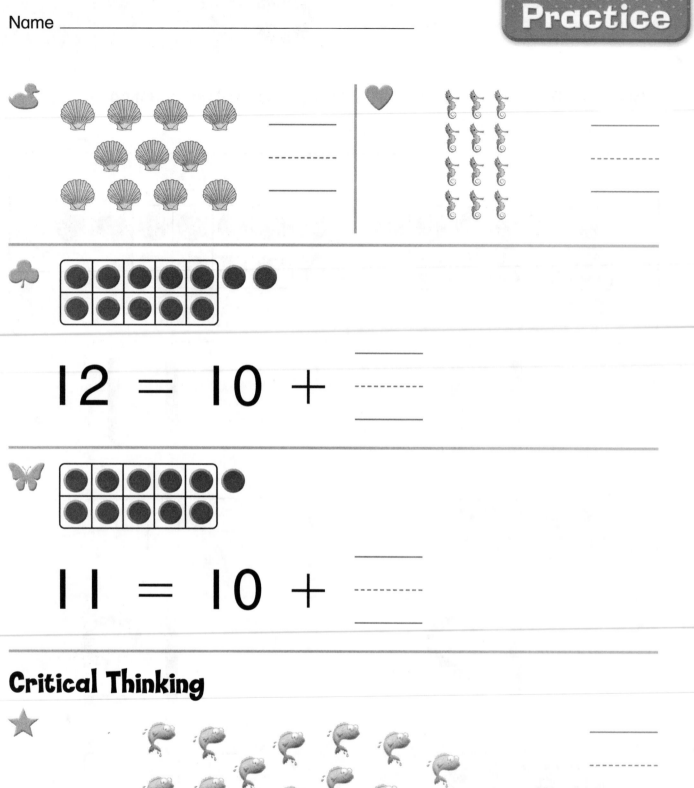

$$12 = 10 + \text{------}$$

$$11 = 10 + \text{------}$$

Critical Thinking

Directions
🦆 ❤️ Count the objects to tell how many. Write the number.
♣️ 🦋 Count the counters. Write how many more to make the number of counters.

Critical Thinking
⭐ Count the objects to tell how many. Write the number. How do you know the number of objects?

C For additional Practice, go to page 223 in this Workbook.
C Then go to Lesson 7-7B, pages 183–184 in this Workbook.

Name _____

Objective: To understand 13 and 14 by reading, writing, counting, and using a ten-frame to model 13 and 14

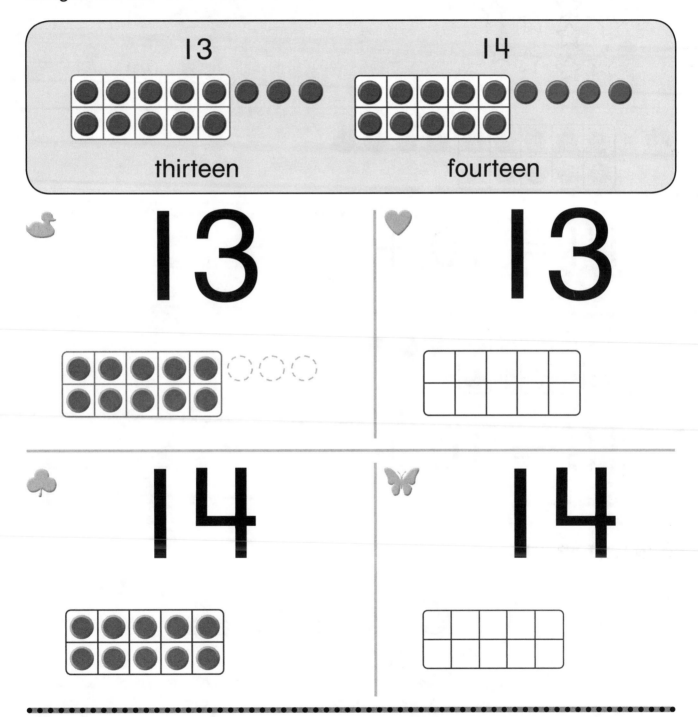

13

thirteen

14

fourteen

13

13

14

14

Directions

Use the ten-frame. Draw more counters to show 13.

Use the ten-frame. Draw more counters to show 14.

Talk It Over

Look at the top of the page. How many counters are in a full ten-frame?
Thirteen is ten and how many more?
Fourteen is ten and how many more?

🦆 ☆☆☆☆ ☆☆☆ ☆☆☆ ☆☆   = = = = = = =

💜   = = = = = = =

♣   (ten frame with counters)

$$14 = 10 + \text{\_\_\_\_}$$

🦋   (ten frame with counters)

$$13 = 10 + \text{\_\_\_\_}$$

Critical Thinking

⭐   (crescent moons)   = = = = = = =

• •

Directions

🦆💜 Count the objects to tell how many. Write the number.

♣🦋 Count the counters. Write how many more to make the number of counters.

Critical Thinking

⭐ Count the objects to tell how many. Write the number. How do you know the number of objects?

C For additional Practice, go to page 224 in this Workbook.
C Then go to Lesson 7-7C, pages 185–186 in this Workbook.

Name _____

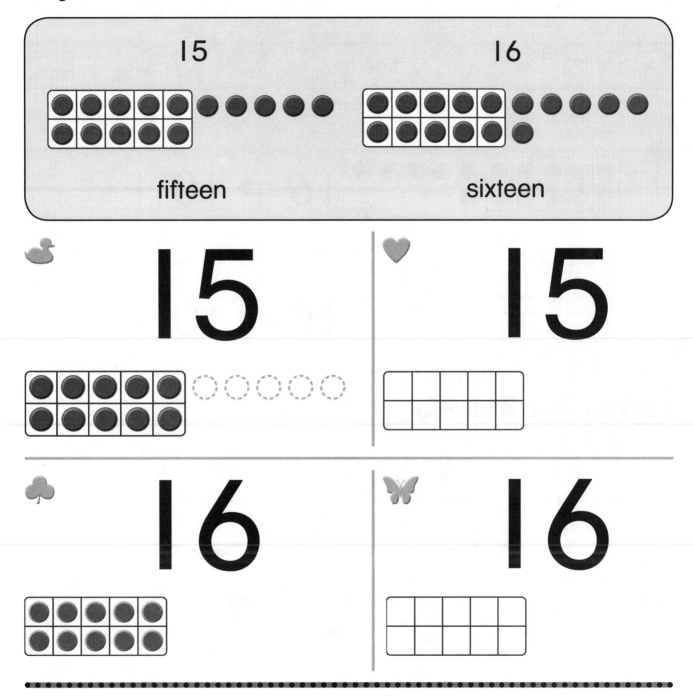
Objective: To understand 15 and 16 by reading, writing, counting, and using a ten-frame to model 15 and 16

15

fifteen

16

sixteen

15

15

16

16

Directions

🦆❤️ Use the ten-frame. Draw more counters to show 15.

♣️🦋 Use the ten-frame. Draw more counters to show 16.

Talk It Over

If 15 is one more than 14, what is one more than 15? Why?

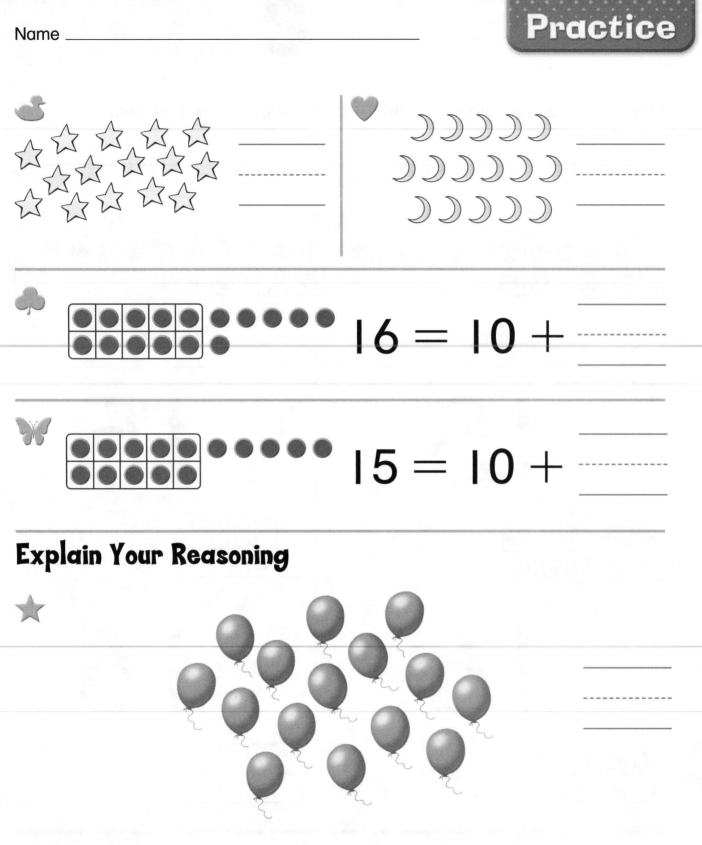

$16 = 10 +$ _____

$15 = 10 +$ _____

Explain Your Reasoning

_____

Directions

Count the objects to tell how many. Write the number.

Count the counters. Write how many more to make the number of counters.

Explain Your Reasoning

★ Count the objects to tell how many. Write the number. How did you know what number to write?

C For additional Practice, go to page 225 in this Workbook.
C Then go to Lesson 7-7D, pages 187–188 in this Workbook.

Name _____

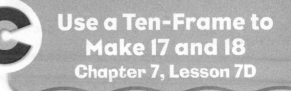
Objective: To understand 17 and 18 by reading, writing, counting, and using a ten-frame to model 17 and 18

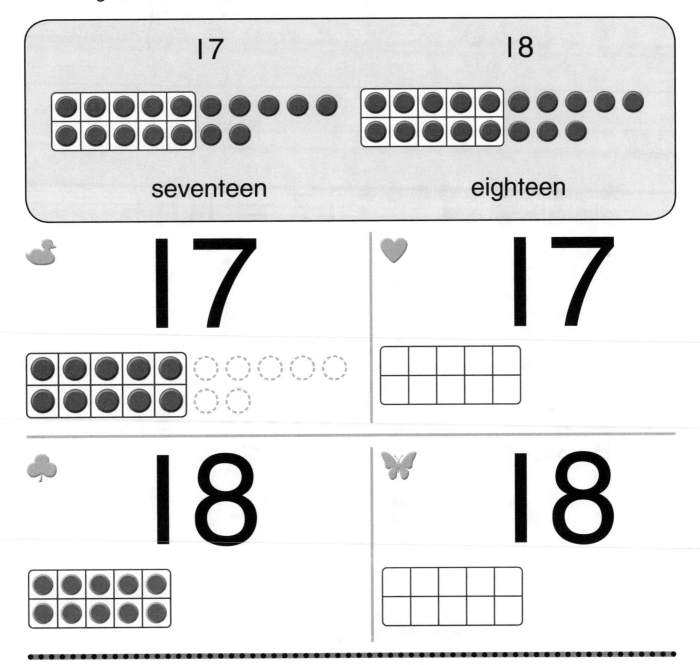

Directions

🦆❤️ Use the ten-frame. Draw more counters to show 17.

♣️🦋 Use the ten-frame. Draw more counters to show 18.

Talk It Over

Look at the picture at the top of the page. Which number is greater, seventeen or eighteen? How do you know?

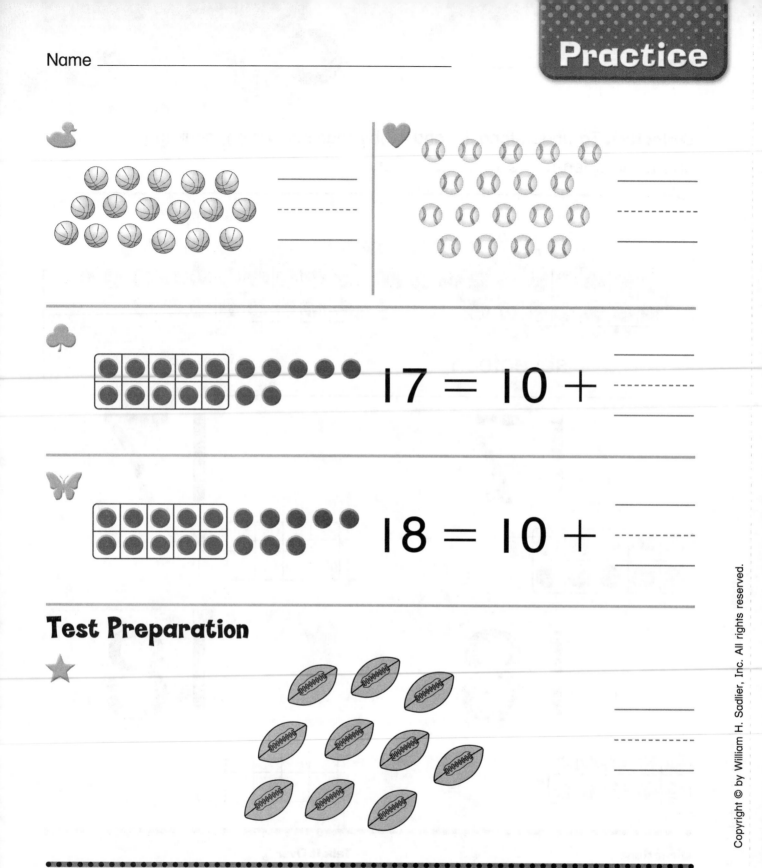

🦆 _____

♥ _____

♣ $17 = 10 +$ _____

🦋 $18 = 10 +$ _____

Test Preparation

⭐ _____

Directions

🦆♥ Count the objects to tell how many. Write the number.

♣🦋 Count the counters. Write how many more to make the number.

Test Preparation

⭐ Count the objects. How many more objects are needed to make 18? Write the number.

C For additional Practice, go to page 226 in this Workbook.
C Then go to Lesson 7-7E, pages 189–190 in this Workbook.

Name _____

Objective: To understand 19 and 20 by reading, writing, counting, and using a ten-frame to model 19 and 20

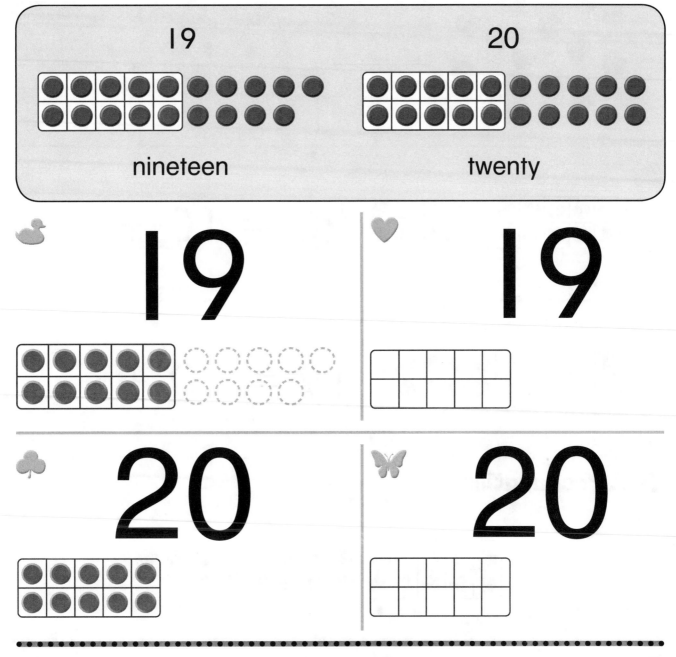

19	20
nineteen	twenty

- -

Directions

🦆❤️ Use the ten-frame. Draw more counters to show 19 counters.

♣🦋 Use the ten-frame. Draw more counters to show 20 counters.

Talk It Over

How many groups of ten are in 20?
How do you know?

Name _____

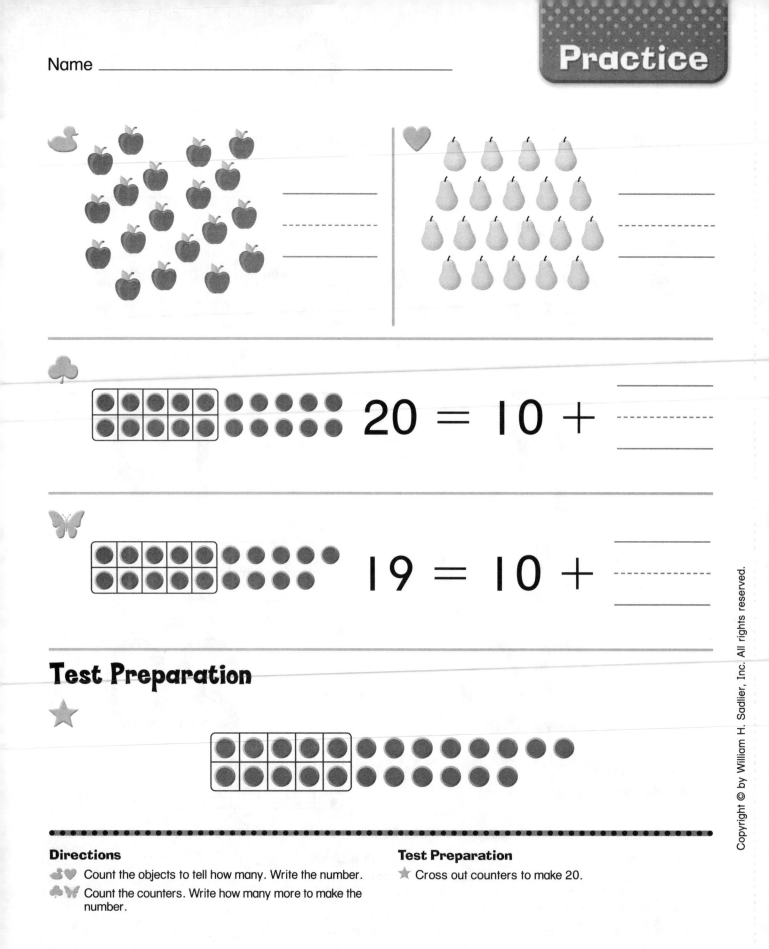

$$20 = 10 +$$

$$19 = 10 +$$

Test Preparation

Directions

Count the objects to tell how many. Write the number.

Count the counters. Write how many more to make the number.

Test Preparation

⭐ Cross out counters to make 20.

For additional Practice, go to page 227 in this Workbook.
Then go to Lesson 7-8, pages 253–254 in the Student Book.

Name _____

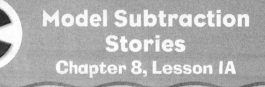
Objective: To model subtraction using objects, stories, and expressions

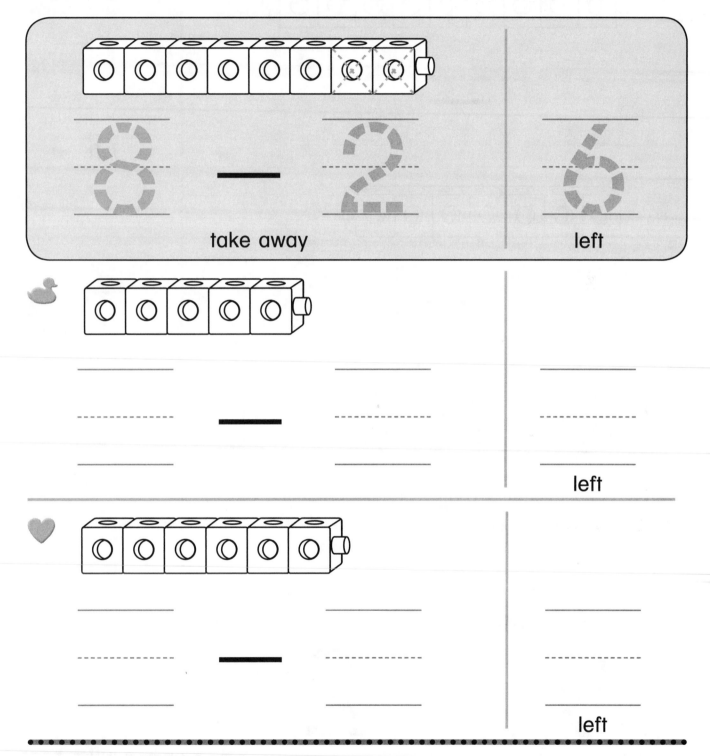

take away   left

left

left

Directions

🦆❤️ Listen to the story. Model the story with connecting cubes. Cross out the part you take away. Write the subtraction. Then write how many are left.

Talk It Over

How do your models show take-away stories?

Name _____

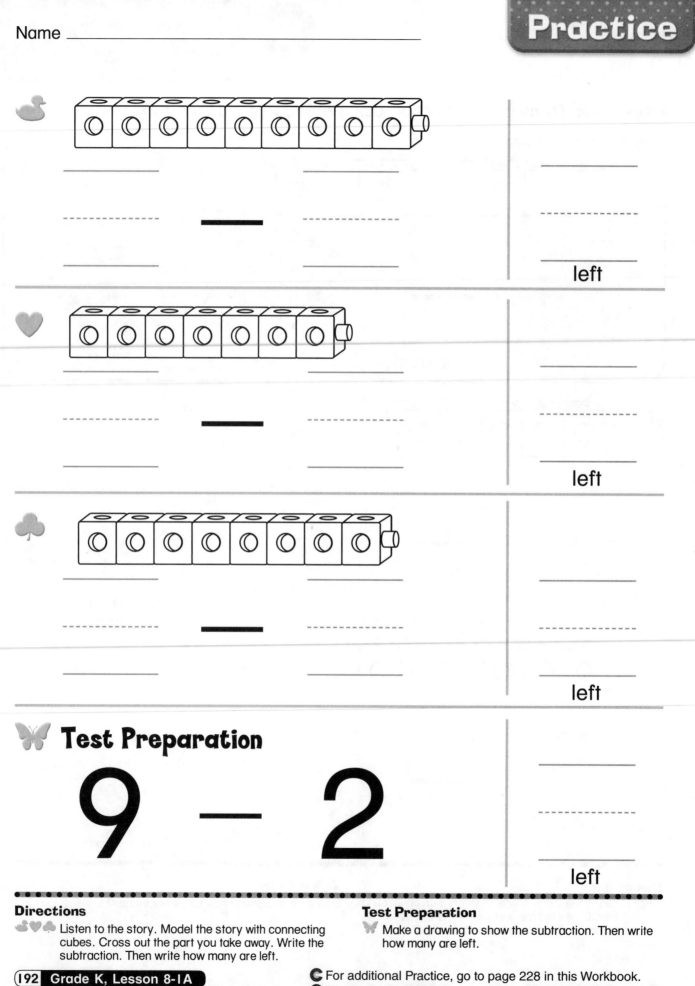

Practice

left

left

left

Test Preparation

9 – 2

left

Directions

Listen to the story. Model the story with connecting cubes. Cross out the part you take away. Write the subtraction. Then write how many are left.

Test Preparation

Make a drawing to show the subtraction. Then write how many are left.

192 Grade K, Lesson 8-1A

C For additional Practice, go to page 228 in this Workbook.
C Then go to Lesson 8-2, pages 271–272 in the Student Book.

Name _____

Objective: To use a bar model to subtract

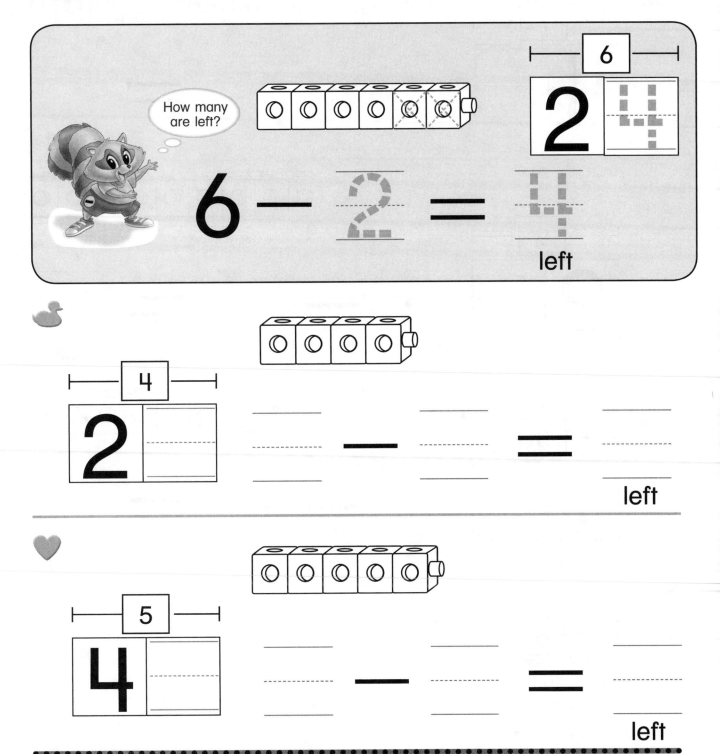

How many are left?

$$6 - 2 = 4$$

left

4

2

$$2 \quad - \quad = \quad$$

left

5

4

$$\quad - \quad = \quad$$

left

Directions
Listen to the story. Cross out cubes to show the part you take away. Complete the bar model. Then write the number sentence to show how many are left.

Talk It Over
How does the bar model help you find how many are left?

Name _____

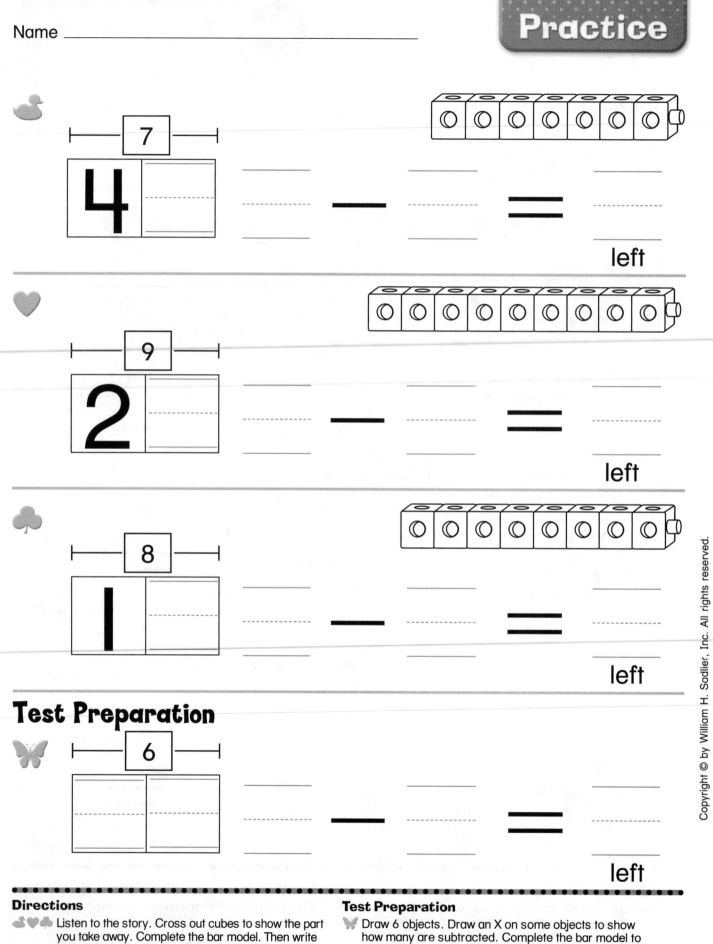

🦆

7

4 | | ____ — ____ = ____

left

❤

9

2 | | ____ — ____ = ____

left

♣

8

1 | | ____ — ____ = ____

left

Test Preparation

🦋

6

____ — ____ = ____

left

Directions

🦆❤♣ Listen to the story. Cross out cubes to show the part you take away. Complete the bar model. Then write the number sentence to show how many are left.

Test Preparation

🦋 Draw 6 objects. Draw an X on some objects to show how many are subtracted. Complete the bar model to show the subtraction. Then write the number sentence.

C For additional Practice, go to page 229 in this Workbook.
C Then go to Lesson 8-6, pages 281–282 in the Student Book.

Name _____

Objective: To describe multiple measurable attributes of the same object

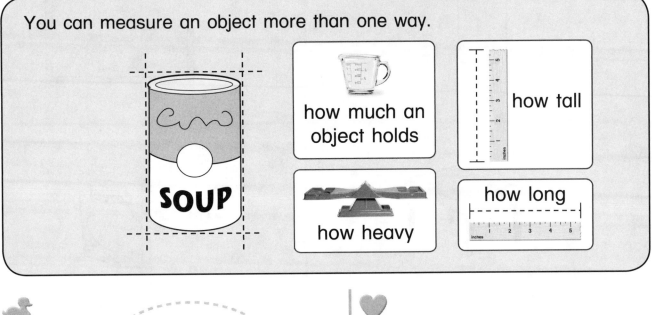

You can measure an object more than one way.

SOUP

how much an object holds

how heavy

how tall

how long

MILK

Directions

🦆 Circle the object if you could measure how much it holds. Put an X on the object if you could measure how long it is.

💜 Circle the object if you could measure how much it weighs. Put an X on the object if you could measure how much it holds.

♣ Circle the object if you could measure how long it is. Put an X on the object if you could measure how much it weighs.

🦋 Circle the object if you could measure how much it holds. Put an X on the object if you could measure how tall it is.

Talk It Over

Discuss what else you could measure for each object above. Name other objects that you could measure how long it is, how tall it is, how much it weighs, and how much it can hold.

Name _____

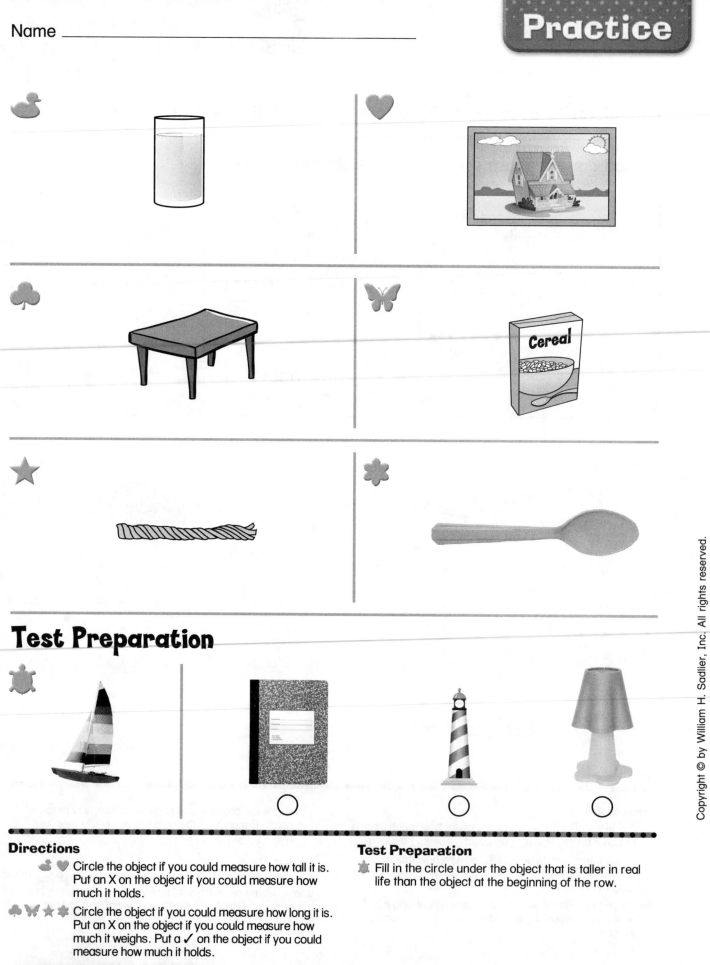

Test Preparation

Directions

🦆 💜 Circle the object if you could measure how tall it is. Put an X on the object if you could measure how much it holds.

♣ 🦋 ⭐ ✿ Circle the object if you could measure how long it is. Put an X on the object if you could measure how much it weighs. Put a ✓ on the object if you could measure how much it holds.

Test Preparation

🐢 Fill in the circle under the object that is taller in real life than the object at the beginning of the row.

🌀 For additional Practice, go to page 230 in this Workbook. Then go to Lesson 11-11, pages 387–388 in the Student Book.

Name _____

Objective: To write numbers in order to 100

1	2	3	4	5	6	7	8	9	10
11	12	13	14	15	16	17	18	19	20
21	22	23	24	25	26	27	28	29	30
31	32	33	34	35	36	37	38	39	40
41	42	43	44	45	46	47	48	49	50
51	52	53	54	55	56	57	58	59	60
61	62	63	64	65	66	67	68	69	70
71	72	73	74	75	76	77	78	79	80
81	82	83	84	85	86	87	88	89	90
91	92	93	94	95	96	97	98	99	100

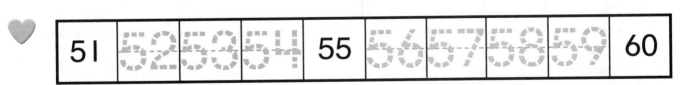

51	52	53	54	55	56	57	58	59	60

Directions

Count from 1 to 100.

Use this part of the hundred chart. Count from 51 to 60.
Trace each number as you say it.

Talk It Over

How is counting from 1 to 100 like counting from 1 to 10?

Name _____

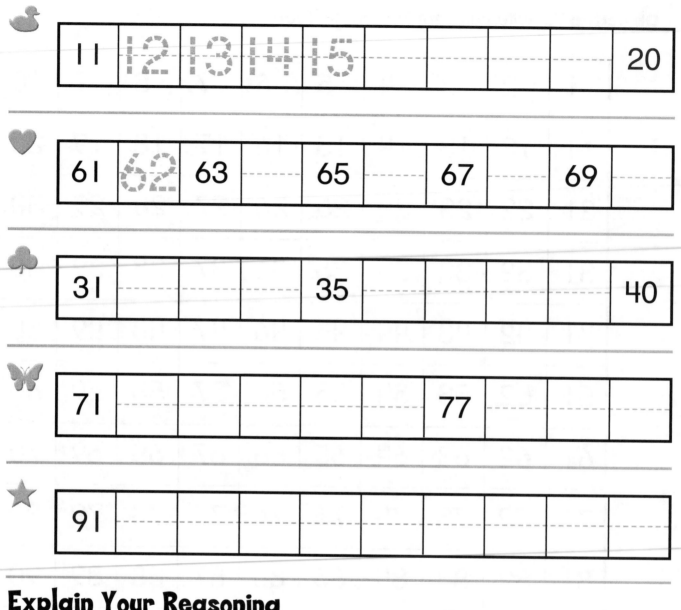

11	12	13	14	15					20

61	62	63		65		67		69	

31				35					40

71						77			

91									

Explain Your Reasoning

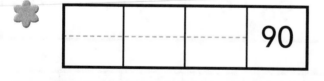

			90

Directions

🦆 Use this part of the hundred chart. Count from 11 to 20. Trace or write each number as you say it.

💜 Use this part of the hundred chart. Count from 61. Trace or write each number as you say it.

♣ Use this part of the hundred chart. Count from 31 to 40. Write each number as you say it.

🦋 Use this part of the hundred chart. Count from 71. Write each number as you say it.

⭐ Use this part of the hundred chart. Count from 91. Write each number as you say it.

Explain Your Reasoning

✿ Use this part of the hundred chart. Write the three numbers you say just before 90 when you count. Explain how you found your answer.

🝚 For additional Practice, go to page 231 in this Workbook.
🝚 Then go to Lesson 12-1B, pages 199–200 in this Workbook.

Recognize Counting Patterns
Chapter 12, Lesson 1B

Objective: To recognize and use patterns in the hundred chart

1	2	3	4	5	6	7	8	9	10
11	12	13	14	15	16	17	18	19	20
21	22	23	24	25	26	27	28	29	30
31	32	33	34	35	36	37	38	39	40
41	42	43	44	45	46	47	48	49	50
51	52	53	54	55	56	57	58	59	60
61	62	63	64	65	66	67	68	69	70
71	72	73	74	75	76	77	78	79	80
81	82	83	84	85	86	87	88	89	90
91	92	93	94	95	96	97	98	99	100

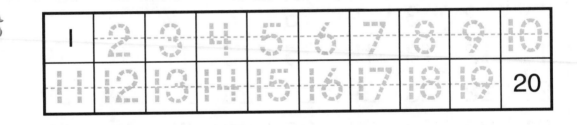

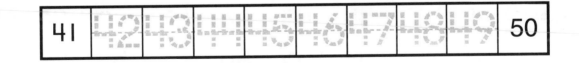

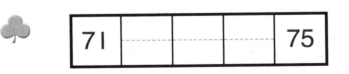

Directions

🦆 Count from 1 to 20. Trace each number as you say it.

💜 Count and trace the numbers from 41 to 50. What patterns do you notice?

♣ Use a pattern to write the missing numbers.

Talk It Over

Look at the hundred chart. Find the numbers that have zeros. What pattern do you see?

1	2	3	4	5	6	7	8	9	
11	12	13	14	15	16	17	18	19	
21	22	23	24	25	26	27	28	29	
31	32	33	34	35	36	37	38	39	
41	42	43	44	45	46	47	48	49	
51	52	53	54	55	56	57	58	59	
61	62	63	64	65	66	67	68	69	
71	72	73	74	75	76	77	78	79	
81	82	83	84	85	86	87	88	89	
91	92	93	94	95	96	97	98	99	

1	2	3	4	5	6	7	8	9	10
11	12	13	14	15	16	17	18	19	20
21	22	23	24	25	26	27	28	29	30
31	32	33	34	35	36	37	38	39	40
41	42	43	44	45	46	47	48	49	50
51	52	53	54	55	56	57	58	59	60
71	72	73	74	75	76	77	78	79	80
81	82	83	84	85	86	87	88	89	90
91	92	93	94	95	96	97	98	99	100

Directions

🦆 💜 Use a pattern to write the missing numbers.

For additional Practice, go to page 232 in this Workbook.
Then go to Lesson 12-2, pages 407–408 in the Student Book.

Name _____

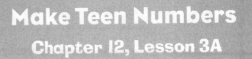
Objective: To decompose numbers from 11 to 19 into a group of 10 ones and some more ones

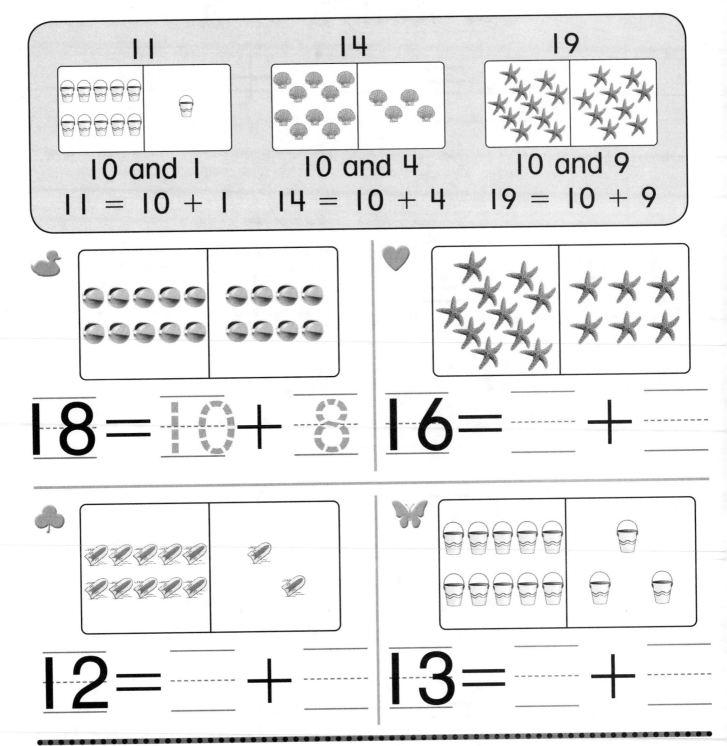

11

10 and 1

11 = 10 + 1

14

10 and 4

14 = 10 + 4

19

10 and 9

19 = 10 + 9

18 = 10 + 8

16 = ___ + ___

12 = ___ + ___

13 = ___ + ___

Directions
Count the objects. Write the number as a group of 10 and some more.

Talk It Over
What are some ways you can make numbers greater than 10?

Name _____

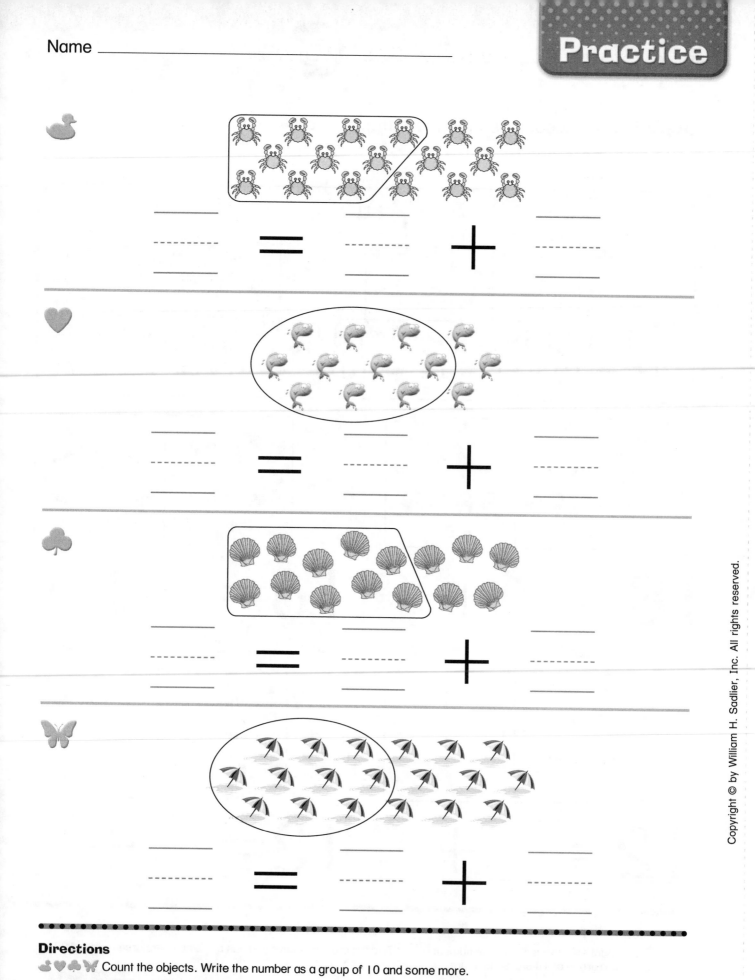

_ _ _ _ _ _   =   _ _ _ _ _ _   +   _ _ _ _ _ _

_ _ _ _ _ _   =   _ _ _ _ _ _   +   _ _ _ _ _ _

_ _ _ _ _ _   =   _ _ _ _ _ _   +   _ _ _ _ _ _

_ _ _ _ _ _   =   _ _ _ _ _ _   +   _ _ _ _ _ _

Directions

🦆♥♣🦋 Count the objects. Write the number as a group of 10 and some more.

C For additional Practice, go to page 233 in this Workbook.
Then go to Lesson 12-4, pages 413–414 in the Student Book.

Additional CCSS Practice

Recognize Solid Figures

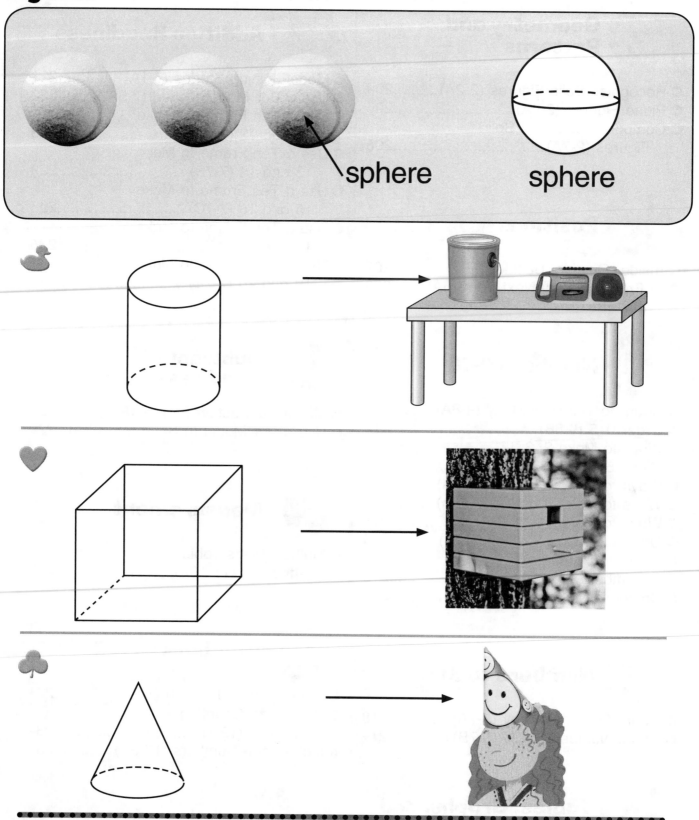

sphere

sphere

Directions

♦ Trace the solid figure. Say the shape of the paint can.

♥ Trace the solid figure. Say the shape of the birdhouse.

♣ Trace the solid figure. Say the shape of the party hat.

204

C Use with Lesson 2-2A, pages 143–144 in this Workbook.
C Then go to Lesson 2-3, pages 41–42 in the Student Book.

Plane Figures

Name _____

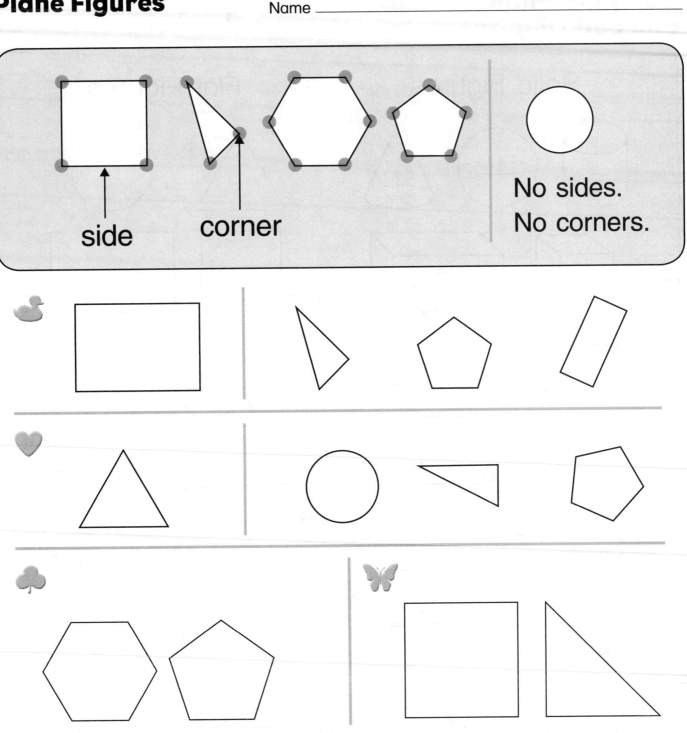

side   corner

No sides.
No corners.

....

Directions

🦆 Color the shape that has the same number of corners as the shape at the beginning of the row.

🖤 Color the shape that has the same number of sides as the shape at the beginning of the row.

♣ Color the shape that has more sides.

🦋 Color the shape that has more corners.

C Use with Lesson 2-4A, pages 145–146 in this Workbook.
C Then go to Lesson 2-5, pages 45–46 in the Student Book.

205

Compare Plane and Solid Figures

Name _____

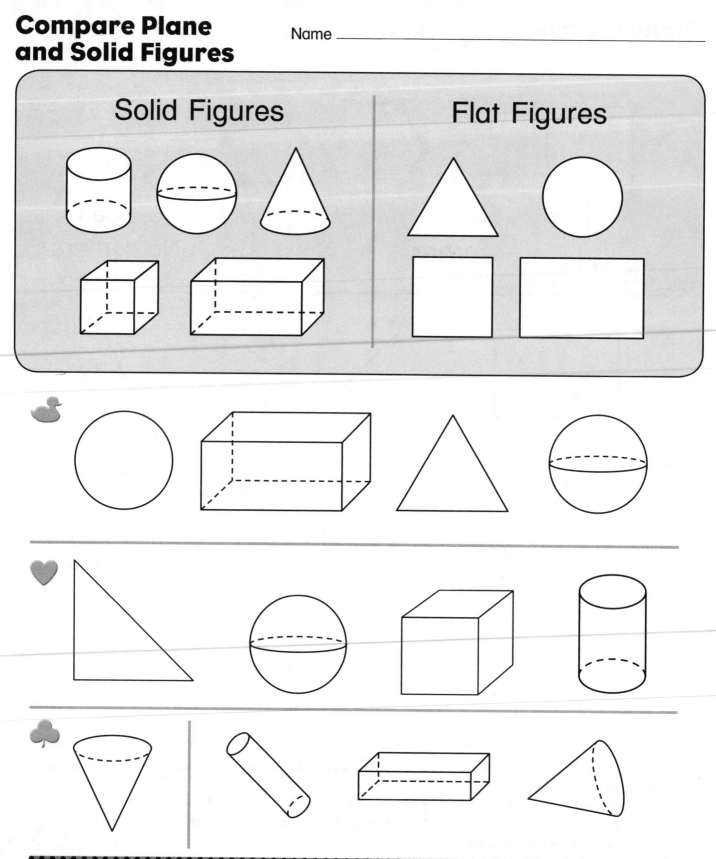

Directions

🦆 Color the shapes that are solid.

♥ Color the shapes that have corners.

♣ Circle the shape that is the same type of shape as the shape at the beginning of the row.

206

C Use with Lesson 2-7A, pages 147–148 in this Workbook.
C Then go to Lesson 2-8, pages 51–52 in the Student Book.

Inside, Outside, Beside

Name _____

inside	outside	beside

Directions

🦆 Circle the picture that shows the egg inside the basket.

💜 Circle the picture that shows the marbles outside the bowl.

♣ Name the shape. Then draw a rectangle beside the shape.

🦋 Name the shape. Then draw a triangle inside the shape.

C Use with Lesson 3-4A, pages 149–150 in this Workbook.
C Then go to Lesson 3-5, pages 87–88 in the Student Book.

207

In Front, Behind, Next To

Name _____

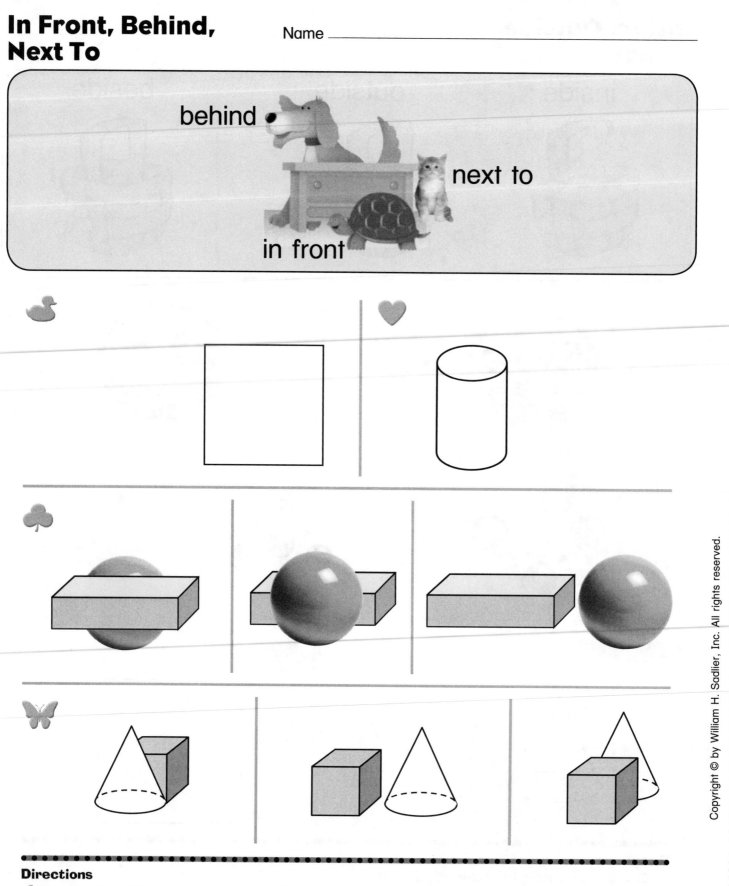

behind

next to

in front

Directions

🦆 Name the shape. Then draw a circle next to the shape.

♥ Name the shape. Then draw a triangle next to the shape.

♣ Circle the picture that shows the rectangular prism in front of a sphere.

🦋 Circle the picture that shows the cone behind a cube.

208

C Use with Lesson 3-5A, pages 151–152 in this Workbook.
C Then go to Lesson 3-6, pages 89–90 in the Student Book.

Count to Tell
How Many

Name _____

Directions

Count the leaves. Write the number that tells how many.

C Use with Lesson 4-8A, pages 153–154 in this Workbook.
C Then go to Lesson 4-8B, pages 155–156 in this Workbook.

209

Order 0–5

| 0 | 1 | 2 | 3 | 4 | 5 |

🦆 🚗 🚗 🚗 🚗 🚗   🚗

_____   _____   _____

- - - - - - - - -   - - - - - - - - -   - - - - - - - - -

_____   _____   _____

❤️ ⚾ ⚾ ⚾ ⚾   ⚾ ⚾   ⚾ ⚾ ⚾

_____   _____   _____

- - - - - - - - -   - - - - - - - - -   - - - - - - - - -

_____   _____   _____

♣️

_____   _____   _____

- - - - - - - - -   - - - - - - - - -   - - - - - - - - -

_____   _____   _____

Directions

🦆❤️ Count how many in each group. Write the numbers.

♣️ Write the numbers in the ❤️ exercise in number order.

C Use with Lesson 4-8B, pages 155–156 in this Workbook.
C Then go to Lesson 4-8C, pages 157–158 in this Workbook.

Ways to Make 2, 3, 4, and 5

Name _____

---

3 is 2 🟦 and 1 ⬜.

3 is 1 🟦 and 2 ⬜.

3 is 3 🟦 and 0 ⬜.

3 is 0 🟦 and 3 ⬜.

🦆

4 is _____ 🟦 and _____ ⬜.

♥

4 is _____ 🟦 and _____ ⬜.

♣

4 is _____ 🟦 and _____ ⬜.

🦋

4 is _____ 🟦 and _____ ⬜.

⭐

5 is _____ 🟦 and _____ ⬜.

✿

5 is _____ 🟦 and _____ ⬜.

Directions

🦆♥ Write numbers to show how to break apart 4 into two parts.

♣🦋 Color to show 4 in different ways. Write numbers to show the two parts.

⭐✿ Color to show 5 in different ways. Write numbers to show the two parts.

Use with Lesson 4-8C, pages 157–158 in this Workbook.
Then go to Lesson 4-9, pages 129–130 in the Student Book.

211

Ways to Make 6 and 7

Name _____

6 is 3 ⬛ and 3 ◻. | 7 is 2 ⬛ and 5 ◻.

🦆

6 is ____ ⬛ and ____ ◻.

♥

6 is ____ ⬛ and ____ ◻.

♣

7 is ____ ⬛ and ____ ◻.

🦋

7 is ____ ⬛ and ____ ◻.

★

7 is ____ ⬛ and ____ ◻.

✿

7 is ____ ⬛ and ____ ◻.

Directions

🦆♥ Write numbers to show how to break apart 6 into two parts.

♣🦋★✿ Color to show 7 in different ways. Write numbers to show the two parts.

🄲 Use with Lesson 4-10A, pages 159–160 in this Workbook.
🄲 Then go to Lesson 4-11, pages 135–136 in the Student Book.

Ways to Make 8 and 9

Name _____

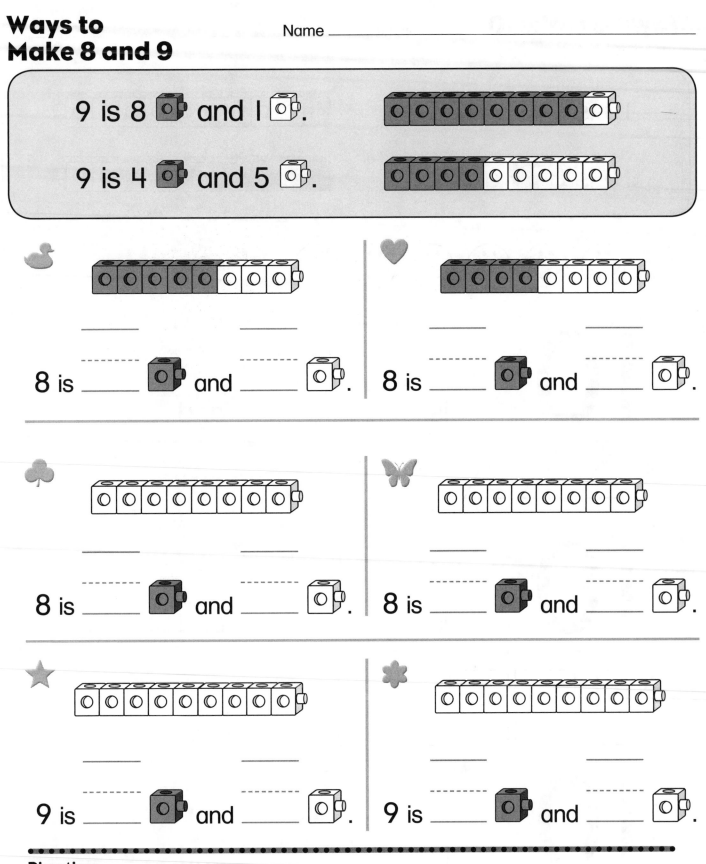

9 is 8 and 1 .

9 is 4 and 5 .

🦆
8 is ____ and ____ .

❤️
8 is ____ and ____ .

♣️
8 is ____ and ____ .

🦋
8 is ____ and ____ .

⭐
9 is ____ and ____ .

✿
9 is ____ and ____ .

Directions
🦆❤️ Write numbers to show how to break apart 8 into two parts.

♣️🦋 Color to show 8 in different ways. Write numbers to show the two parts.

⭐✿ Color to show 9 in different ways. Write numbers to show the two parts.

C Use with Lesson 4-11A, pages 161–162 in this Workbook.
C Then go to Lesson 4-12, pages 137–138 in the Student Book.

Ways to Make 10

Name _____

10 is 1 🔲 and 9 ▫️.

10 is 8 🔲 and 2 ▫️.

🦆 ☺ ☺ ☺ ☺ ☺ ☺

10   is _____ and _____ .

♥ △ △ △

10   is _____ and _____ .

♣ ☐ ☐ ☐ ☐ ☐

10   is _____ and _____ .

Directions

🦆♥♣ Draw more of the same shape to make 10. Write the number for each part.

C Use with Lesson 4-12A, pages 163–164 in this Workbook.
C Then go to Lesson 4-12B, pages 165–166 in this Workbook.

One More, One Fewer

① ② ③ ④ ⑤
☆☆☆☆★

One more than
4 ☆ is 5 ☆.

① ② ③ ④ ⑤

⑥
One fewer than
6 ◯ is 5 ◯.

One more than

____ ◯ is ____ ◯.

One more than

____ ◯ is ____ ◯.

One fewer than

____ ◯ is ____ ◯.

One fewer than

____ ◯ is ____ ◯.

♡ ♡ ♡

____
____
____

Directions

Count the counters. Draw one more. Write the numbers.

Count the counters. Cross out one. Write the numbers.

Count the objects. Draw one more. Write the number.

C Use with Lesson 4-12B, pages 165–166 in this Workbook.
C Then go to Lesson 4-12C, pages 167–168 in this Workbook.

Count to
Compare Numbers

Name _____

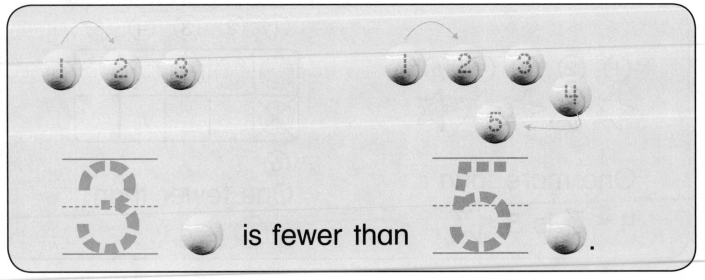

___3___ is fewer than ___5___.

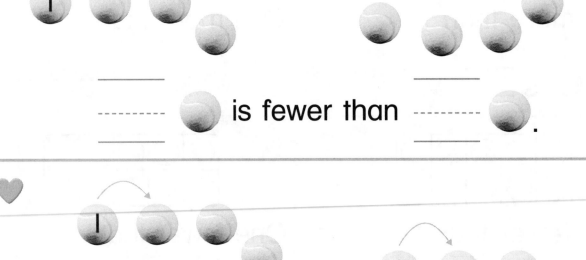

_____ is fewer than _____.

_____ is more than _____.

Directions

🦆 Count the tennis balls on the left. Write the number in each tennis ball as you count. Then write how many below. Now count the tennis balls on the right. Write the number in each tennis ball as you count. Then write how many below. Tell which number is fewer.

💜 Count the tennis balls on the left. Write the number in each tennis ball as you count. Then write how many below. Now count the tennis balls on the right. Write the number in each tennis ball as you count. Then write how many below. Tell which number is more.

216

C Use with Lesson 4-12C, pages 167–168 in this Workbook.
C Then go to Lesson 4-13, pages 139–140 in the Student Book.

Compare Numbers

Name _____

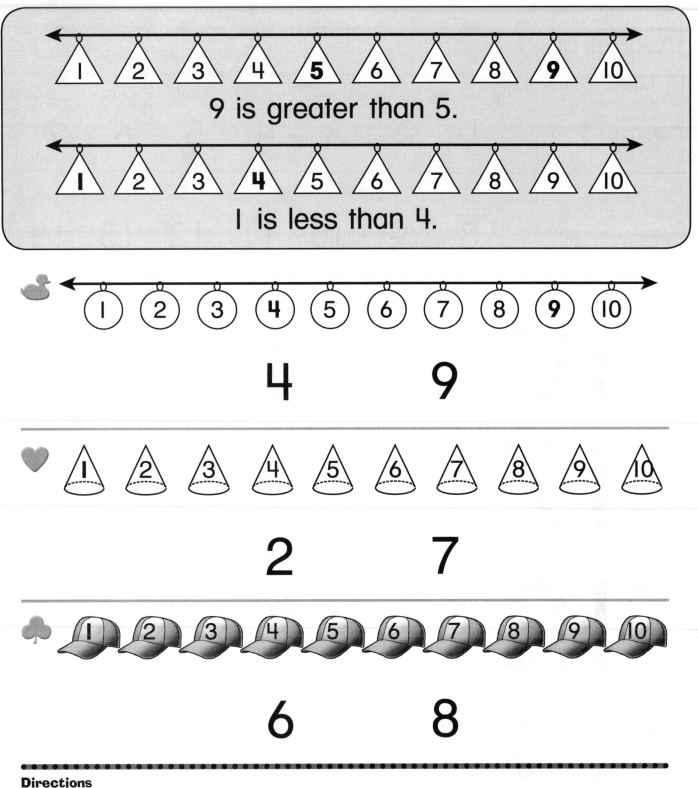

9 is greater than 5.

1 is less than 4.

4   9

2   7

6   8

Directions

🦆 Look at the number line. Circle the number that is greater.

♥ Color the cones with the numbers 2 and 7. Look at the numbers below. Circle the number that is greater.

♣ Color the hats with the numbers 6 and 8. Look at the numbers below. Circle the number that is less.

Use with Lesson 4-14A, pages 169–170 in this Workbook.
Then go to Lesson 4-15, pages 143–144 in the Student Book.

217

Count Out That Many

Name _____

Count out 14 .

1	2	3	4	5	6	7
8	9	10	11	12	13	14

10

17

12

19

Directions
Use counters. Count out the number shown. Draw circles to show the number. Write how many you drew.

Use with Lesson 5-7A, pages 171–172 in this Workbook.
Then go to Lesson 5-7B, pages 173–174 in this Workbook.

Count Numbers to 20

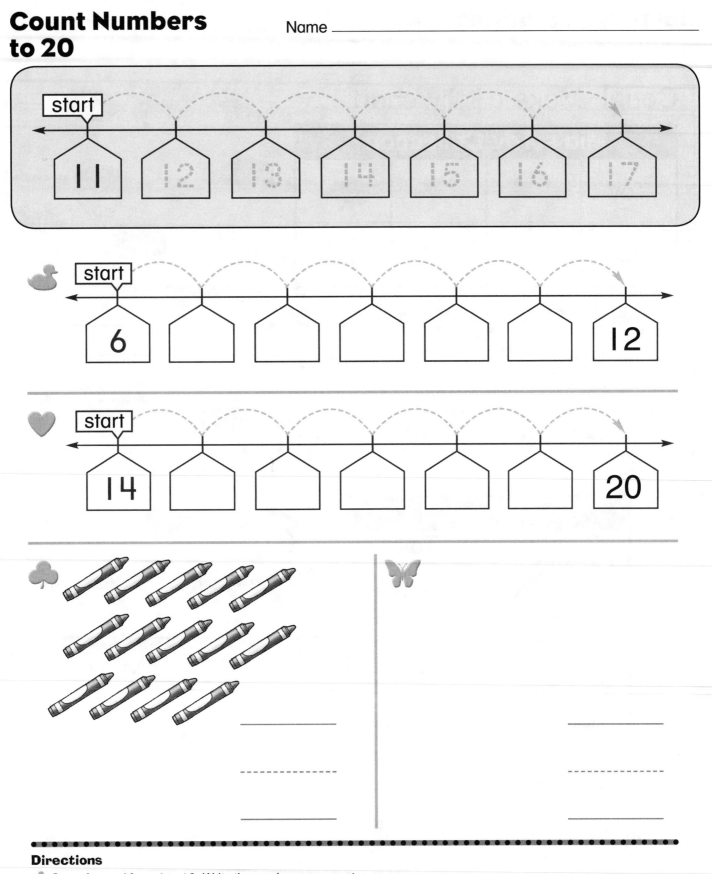

```
start          →
 11  12  13  14  15  16  17
```

start
6   12

start
14   20

Directions

🦆 Count forward from 6 to 12. Write the numbers you count.

💜 Count forward from 14 to 20. Write the numbers you count.

♣ Count the crayons. Write the number. How do you know that your answer is correct?

🦋 Choose a number from 11 through 20. Write the number. Draw that many objects.

C Use with Lesson 5-7B, pages 173–174 in this Workbook.
C Then go to Lesson 5-8, pages 175–176 in the Student Book.

219

Sorting Categories

Name _____

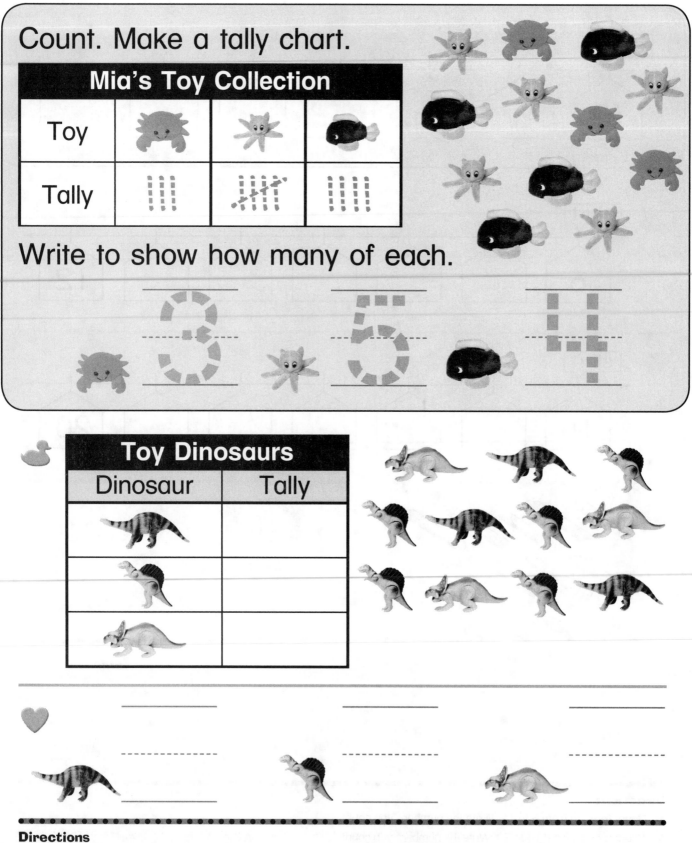

Count. Make a tally chart.

Mia's Toy Collection

Toy	🦀	🐙	🐟
Tally	IIII	JHT	IIII

Write to show how many of each.

3   5   4

Toy Dinosaurs

Dinosaur	Tally
🦕	
🦖	
🦕	

Directions

🦆 Count the toy dinosaurs. Draw tally marks to show how many of each dinosaur.

💜 Count the tally marks in the 🦆 exercise. Write the number next to each toy dinosaur.

C Use with Lesson 6-2A, pages 175–176 in this Workbook.
C Then go to Lesson 6-3, pages 205–206 in the Student Book.

Model Joining Stories

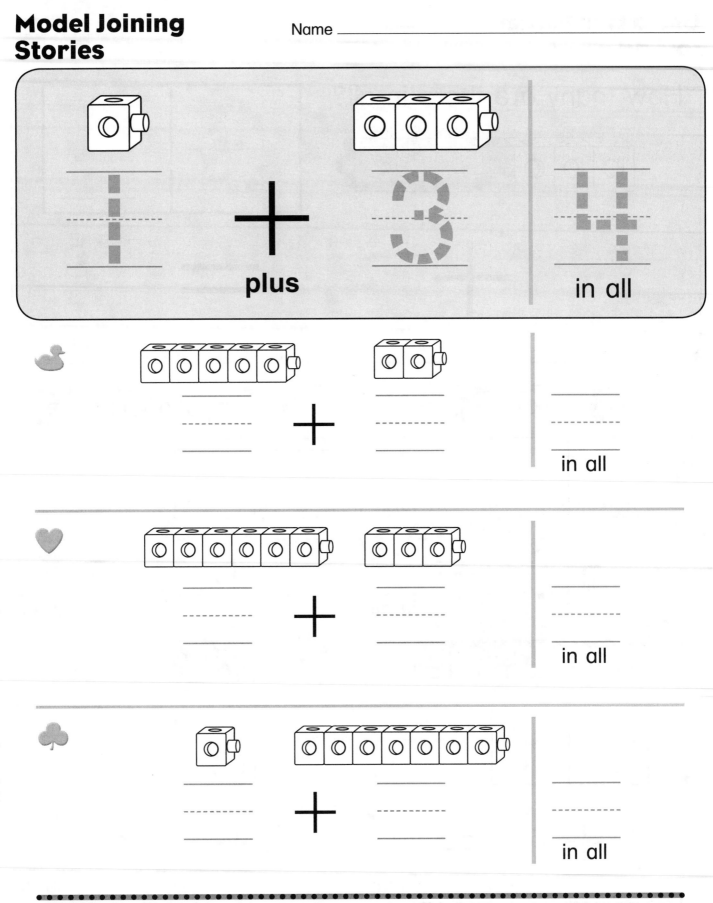

1 + 3

plus

4

in all

🦆

＿＿＿＿ + ＿＿＿＿

＿＿＿＿
in all

♥

＿＿＿＿ + ＿＿＿＿

＿＿＿＿
in all

♣

＿＿＿＿ + ＿＿＿＿

＿＿＿＿
in all

Directions

🎵♥♣ Listen to the story. Model the joining story with connecting cubes.
Write the number in each part. Then write how many in all.

C Use with Lesson 7-1A, pages 177–178 in this Workbook.
C Then go to Lesson 7-2, pages 239–240 in the Student Book.

221

Use a Bar Model to Add

Name _____

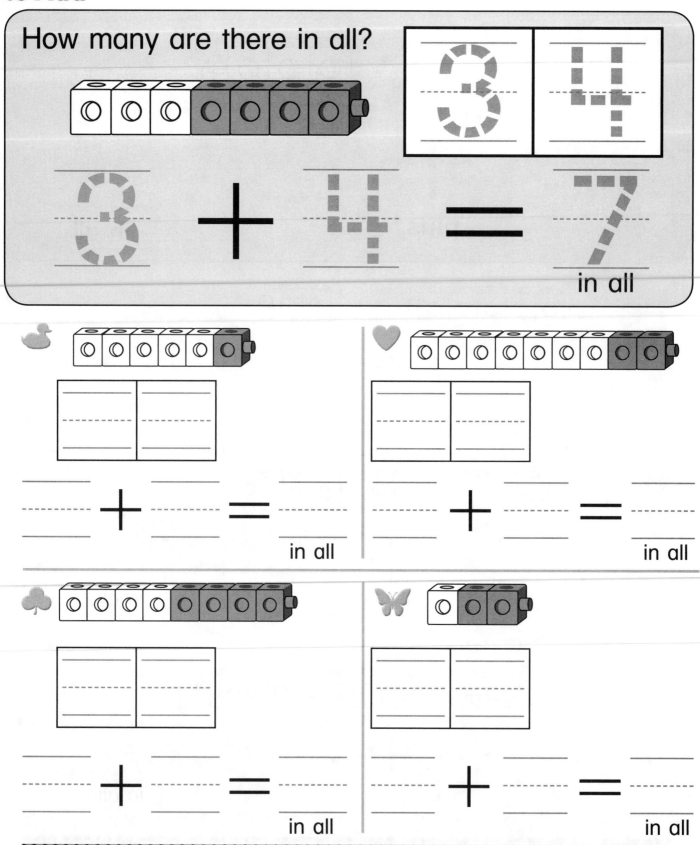

How many are there in all?

3 + 4 = 7

in all

+ =
in all

+ =
in all

+ =
in all

+ =
in all

Directions

Listen to the story. Write the number in each part in the bar model.
Then write a number sentence to show how many in all.

222

C Use with Lesson 7-5A, pages 179–180 in this Workbook.
C Then go to Lesson 7-6, pages 249–250 in the Student Book.

Use a Ten-Frame to Make 11 and 12

Name _____

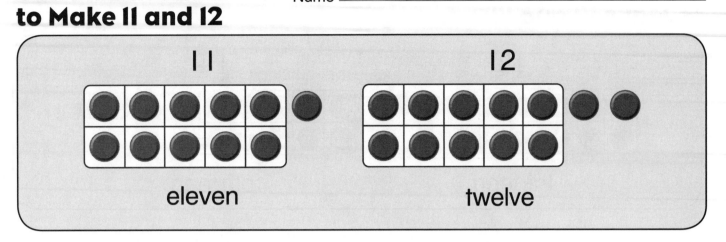

11

eleven

12

twelve

_____
- - - - - -
_____

_____
- - - - - -
_____

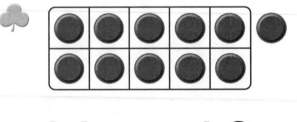

$$11 = 10 + \underline{}$$

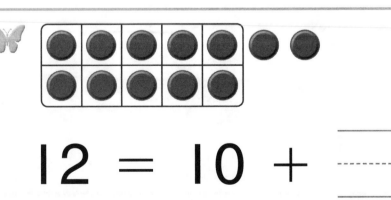

$$12 = 10 + \underline{}$$

Directions

Count the objects to tell how many. Write the number.

Count the counters. Write how many more to make the number of counters.

Use with Lesson 7-7A, pages 181–182 in this Workbook.
Then go to Lesson 7-7B, pages 183–184 in this Workbook.

223

Use a Ten-Frame to Make 13 and 14

Name _____

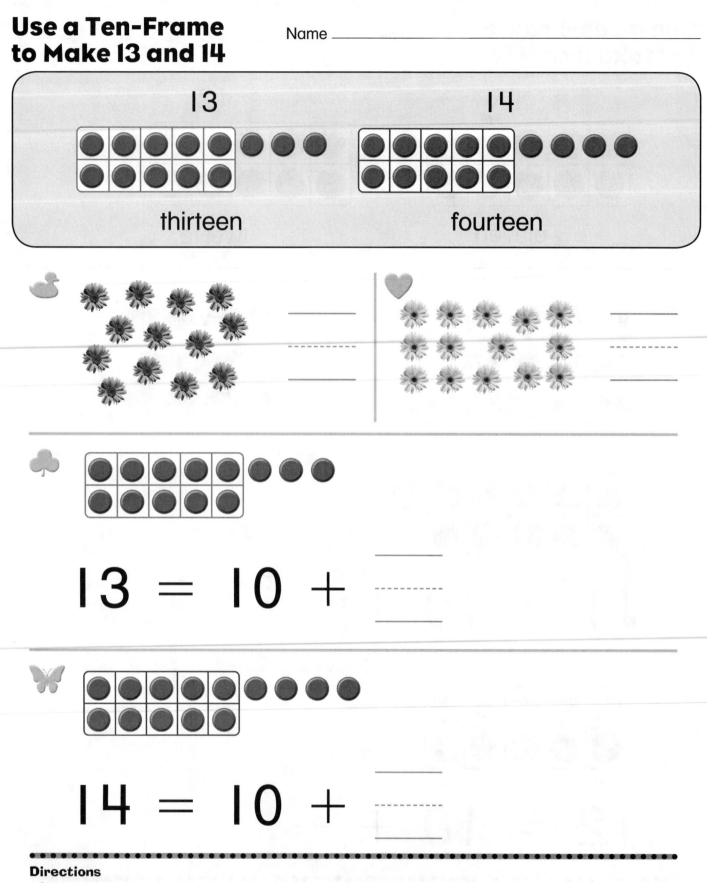

13	14
thirteen	fourteen

13 = 10 + _____

14 = 10 + _____

Directions

Count the objects to tell how many. Write the number.

Count the counters. Write how many more to make the number of counters.

Use with Lesson 7-7B, pages 183–184 in this Workbook.
Then go to Lesson 7-7C, pages 185–186 in this Workbook.

Use a Ten-Frame to Make 15 and 16

Name _____

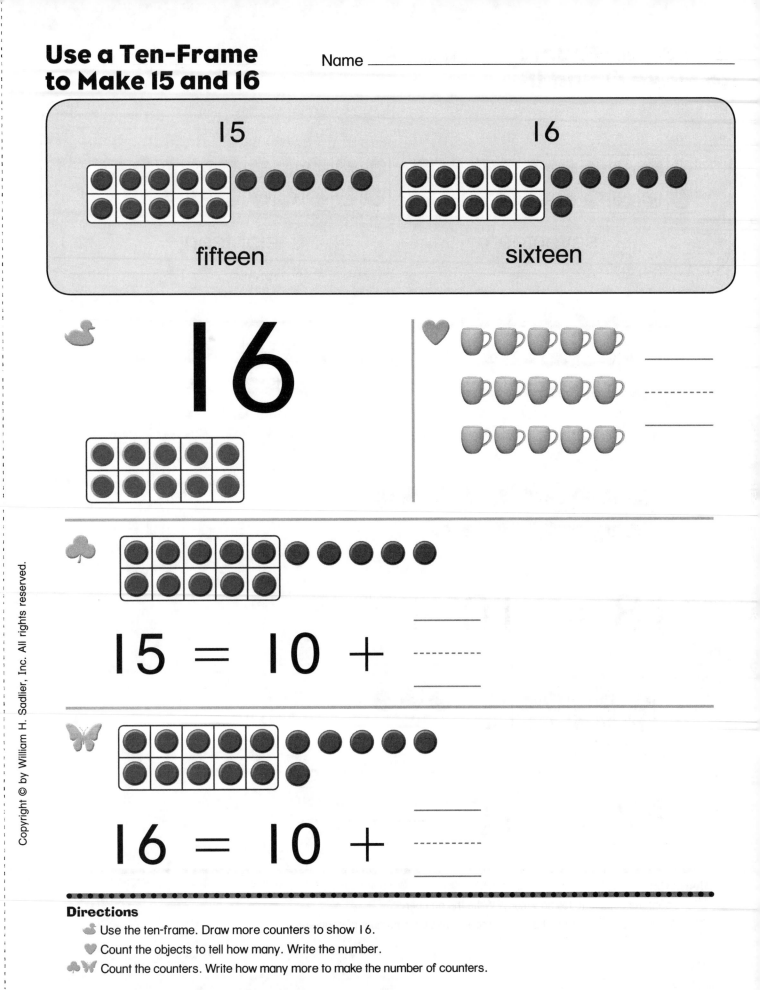

15

fifteen

16

sixteen

16

15 = 10 + ____

16 = 10 + ____

Directions

🦆 Use the ten-frame. Draw more counters to show 16.

♥ Count the objects to tell how many. Write the number.

♣🦋 Count the counters. Write how many more to make the number of counters.

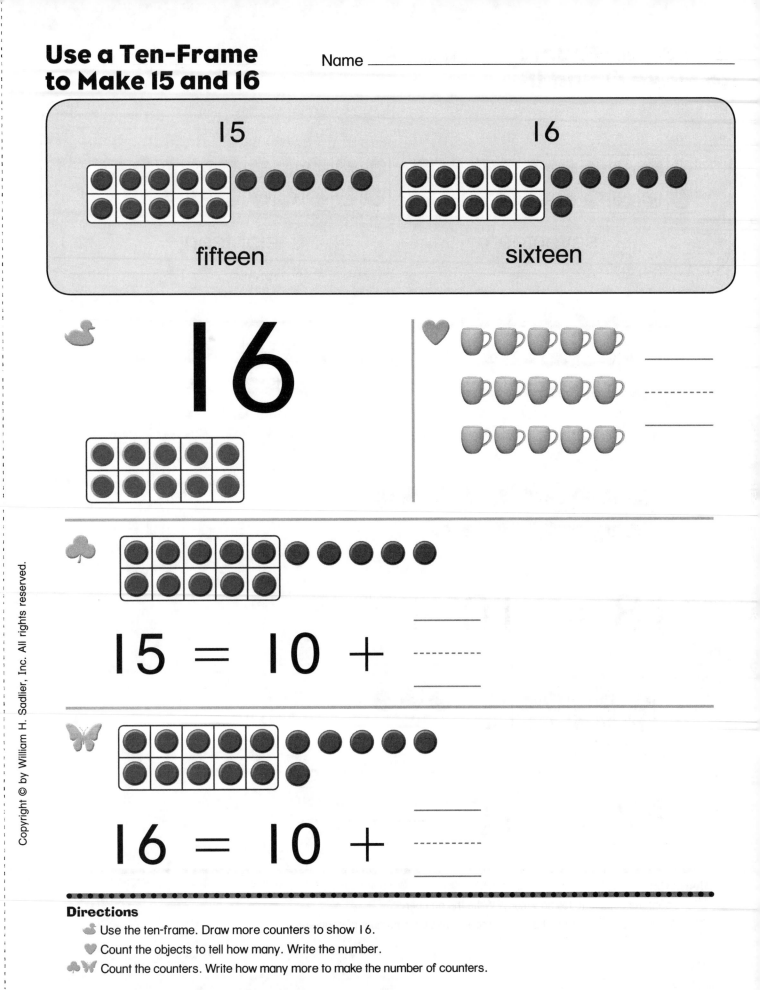Use with Lesson 7-7C, pages 185–186 in this Workbook.

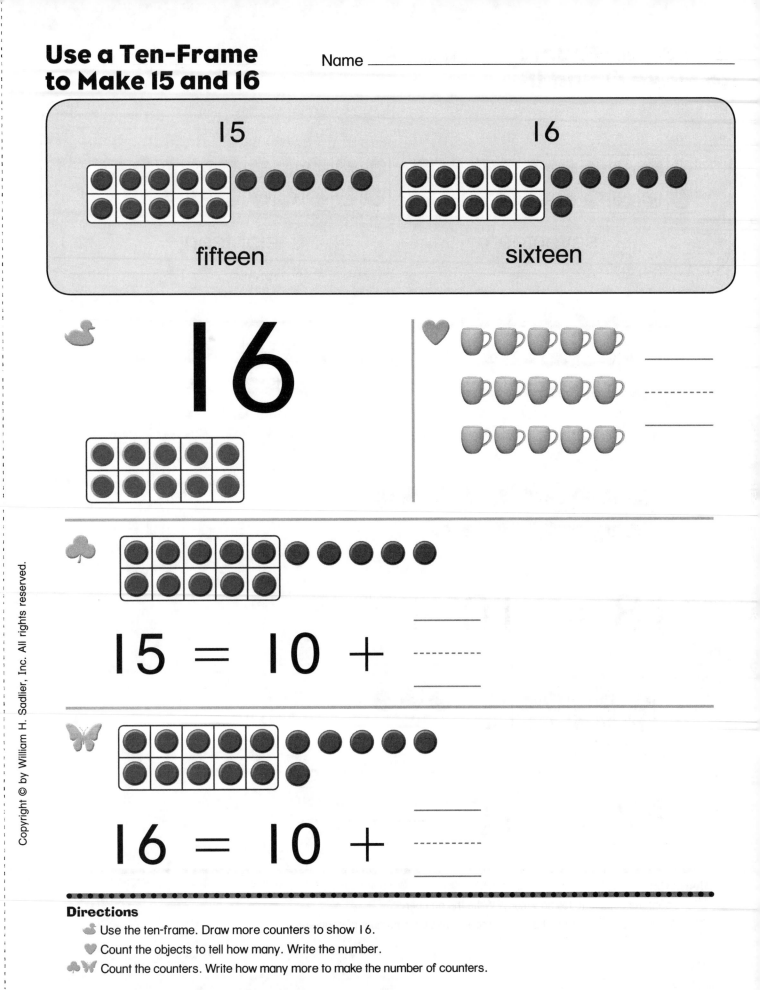Then go to Lesson 7-7D, pages 187–188 in this Workbook.

225

Use a Ten-Frame to Make 17 and 18

Name _____

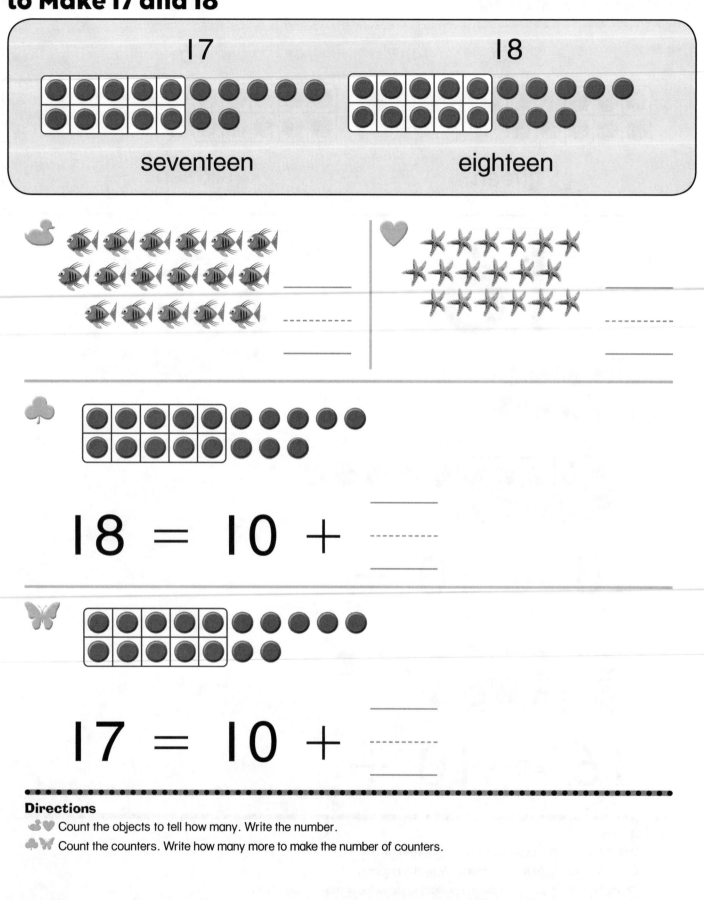

17	18
seventeen	eighteen

18 = 10 + _____

17 = 10 + _____

Directions

Count the objects to tell how many. Write the number.

Count the counters. Write how many more to make the number of counters.

Use with Lesson 7-7D, pages 187–188 in this Workbook.
Then go to Lesson 7-7E, pages 189–190 in this Workbook.

Use a Ten-Frame to Make 19 and 20

Name _____

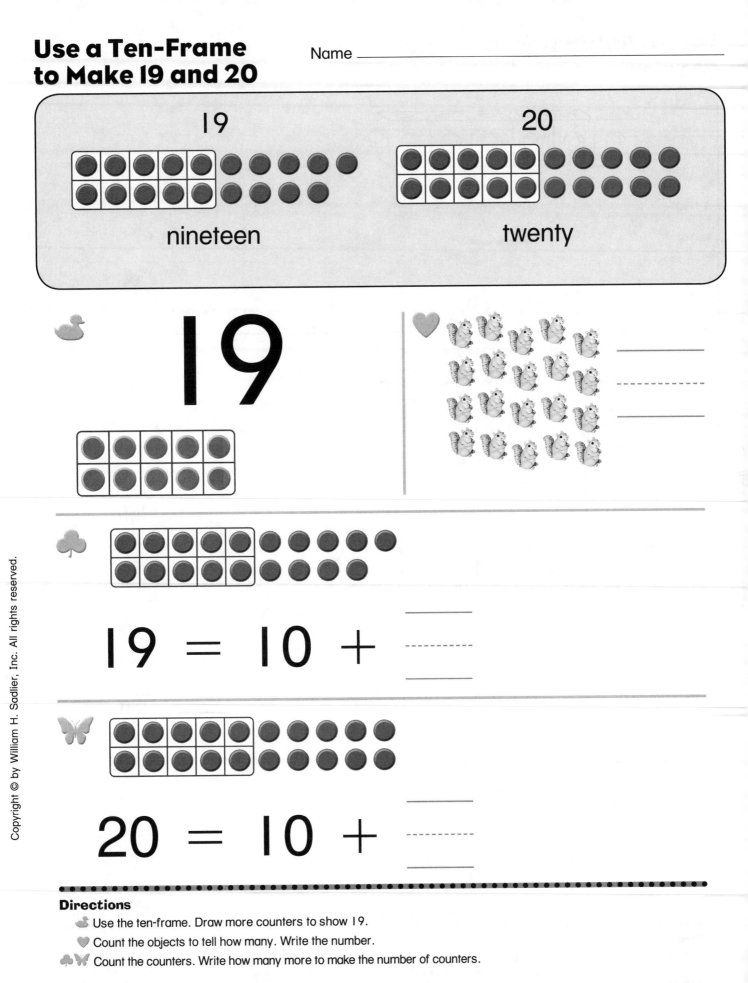

19	20
nineteen	twenty

19

19 = 10 + ____

20 = 10 + ____

Directions

Use the ten-frame. Draw more counters to show 19.

Count the objects to tell how many. Write the number.

Count the counters. Write how many more to make the number of counters.

Use with Lesson 7-7E, pages 189–190 in this Workbook.
Then go to Lesson 7-8, pages 253–254 in the Student Book.

Model Subtraction Stories

Name _____

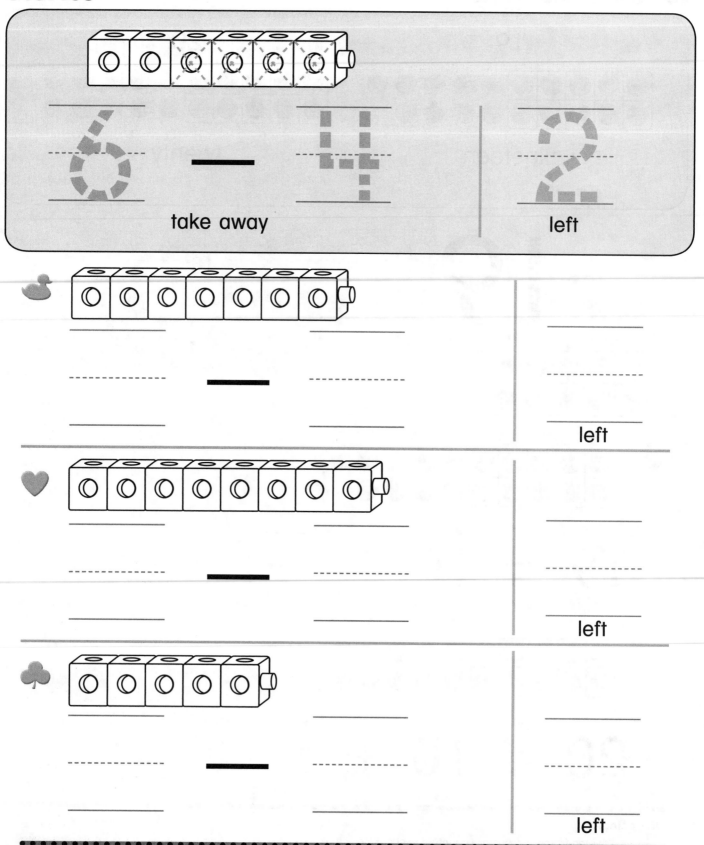

6 − 4

take away

2

left

🦆

___ − ___

___ left

❤️

___ − ___

___ left

♣️

___ − ___

___ left

Directions

♣️❤️♣️ Listen to the story. Model the story with connecting cubes. Cross out the part you take away.
Write the subtraction. Then write how many are left.

☾ Use with Lesson 8-1A, pages 191–192 in this Workbook.
☾ Then go to Lesson 8-2, pages 271–272 in the Student Book.

Use a Bar Model to Subtract

Name _____

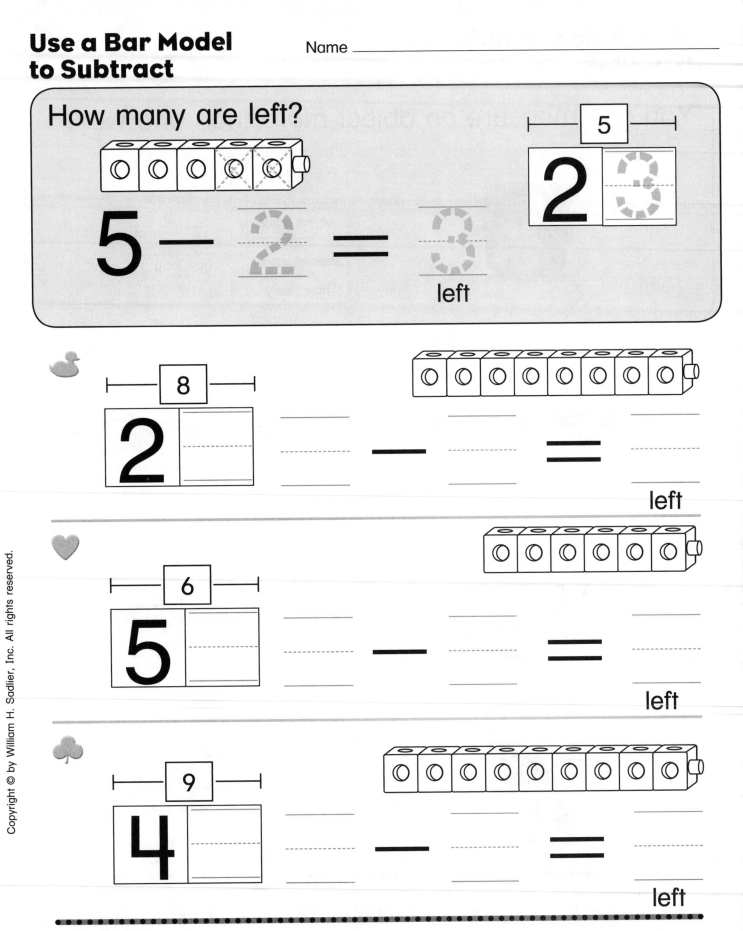

How many are left?

5 — 2 = 3
left

5
2 3

8
2

— =
left

6
5

— =
left

9
4

— =
left

Directions

🦆❤️♣ Listen to the story. Cross out cubes to show the part you take away. Complete the bar model.
Then write the number sentence to show how many are left.

C Use with Lesson 8-5A, pages 193–194 in this Workbook.
C Then go to Lesson 8-6, pages 281–282 in the Student Book.

Multiple Measurable Attributes

Name _____

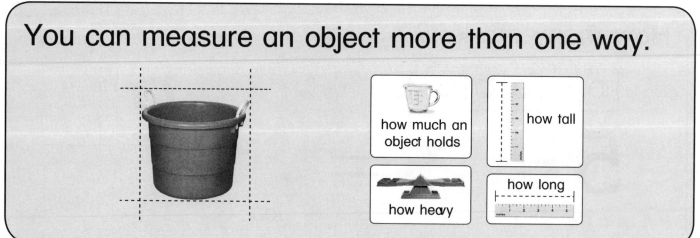

You can measure an object more than one way.

how much an object holds   how tall

how heavy   how long

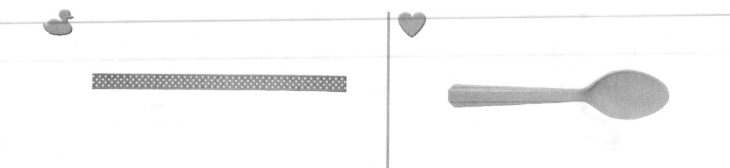

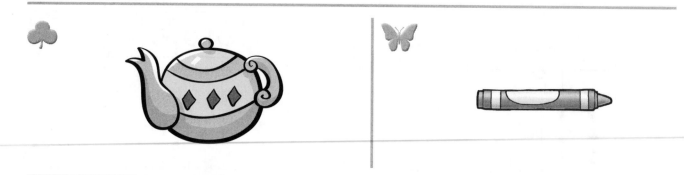

●●

Directions

🦆 💜 Circle the object if you could measure how long it is. Put a [✓ mark] on the object if you could measure how much it holds.

♣ 🦋 ⭐ ❀ Circle the object if you could measure how long it is. Put an X on the object if you could measure how much it weighs. Put a ✓ on the object if you could measure how much it holds.

230

C Use with Lesson 11-10A, pages 195–196 in this Workbook.
Then go to Lesson 11-11, pages 387–388 in the Student Book.

Count Forward to 100

1	2	3	4	5	6	7	8	9	10
11	12	13	14	15	16	17	18	19	20
21	22	23	24	25	26	27	28	29	30
31	32	33	34	35	36	37	38	39	40
41	42	43	44	45	46	47	48	49	50
51	52	53	54	55	56	57	58	59	60
61	62	63	64	65	66	67	68	69	70
71	72	73	74	75	76	77	78	79	80
81	82	83	84	85	86	87	88	89	90
91	92	93	94	95	96	97	98	99	100

41					46				50

81							88		90

51									

Directions

Count from 1 to 100.

Use this part of the hundred chart. Count from 41 to 50. Write each number as you say it.

Use this part of the hundred chart. Count from 81. Write each number as you say it.

Use this part of the hundred chart. Count from 51. Write each number as you say it.

C Use with Lesson 12-1A, pages 197–198 in this Workbook.
C Then go to Lesson 12-1B, pages 199–200 in this Workbook.

231

Recognize Counting Patterns

1	2	3	4	5	6	7	8	9	10
11	12	13	14	15	16	17	18	19	20
21	22	23	24	25	26	27	28	29	30
31	32	33	34	35	36	37	38	39	40
41	42	43	44	45	46	47	48	49	50
51	52	53	54	55	56	57	58	59	60
61	62	63	64	65	66	67	68	69	70
71	72	73	74	75	76	77	78	79	80
81	82	83	84	85	86	87	88	89	90
91	92	93	94	95	96	97	98	99	100

🦆	81				85

♥	46				50

♣	1	2	3	4	5	6		8	9	10
	11	12	13	14	15	16		18	19	20
	21	22	23	24	25	26		28	29	30
	31	32	33	34	35	36		38	39	40
	41	42	43	44	45	46		48	49	50
	51	52	53	54	55	56		58	59	60
	61	62	63	64	65	66		68	69	70
	71	72	73	74	75	76		78	79	80
	81	82	83	84	85	86		88	89	90
	91	92	93	94	95	96		98	99	100

Directions

 Use a pattern to write the missing numbers.

♣ Use with Lesson 12-1B, pages 199–200 in this Workbook.
♣ Then go to Lesson 12-2, pages 407–408 in the Student Book.

Make Teen Numbers

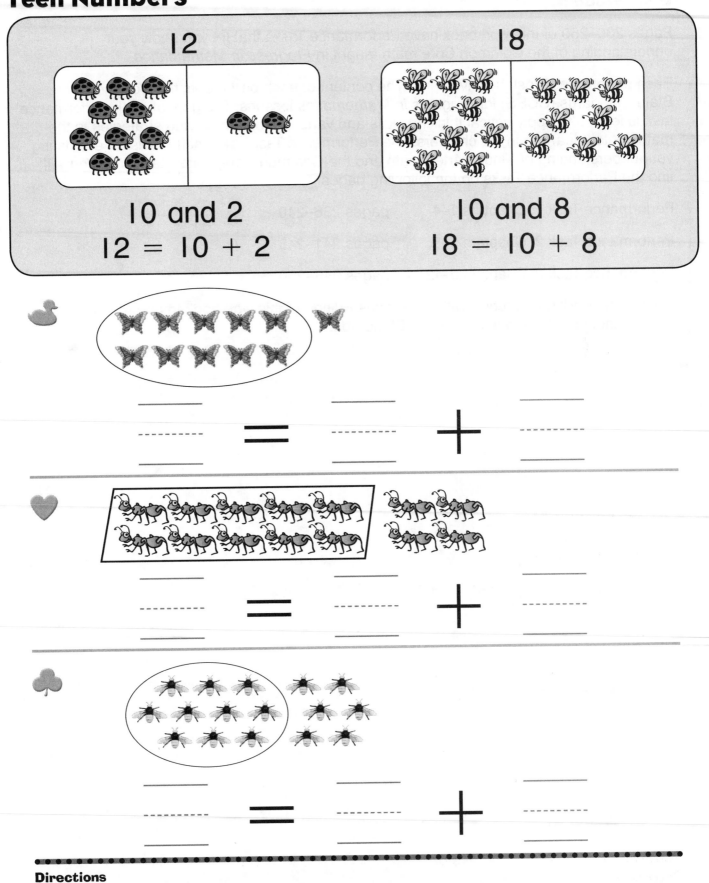

12

10 and 2
12 = 10 + 2

18

10 and 8
18 = 10 + 8

_____ _____ _____
----- = ----- + -----

_____ _____ _____
----- = ----- + -----

_____ _____ _____
----- = ----- + -----

Directions

Count the objects. Write the number as a group of 10 and some more.

C Use with Lesson 12-3A, pages 201–202 in this Workbook.
Then go to Lesson 12-4, pages 413–414 in the Student Book.

233

Dear Student,

Pages 236–250 of this workbook have Performance Tasks that let you show your understanding of the Common Core math taught in *Progress in Mathematics.*

Each performance task has five parts. The content of each part meets the Common Core State Standards (CCSS) for *Progress in Mathematics* lessons. The goal of each performance task is for you to apply critical thinking skills and various problem-solving strategies to the math content learned in the chapters. The Performance Tasks are useful tools for evaluating your understanding of Kindergarten math and the Common Core State Standards. You will find the Performance Tasks on the following pages.

Performance Task 1: Chapters 1–4   pages 236–240

Performance Task 2: Chapters 5–8   pages 241–245

Performance Task 3: Chapters 9–12   pages 246–250

Your teacher will use a rubric in the Teacher's Edition of this workbook to record your understanding of Common Core State Standards.

Performance Task Contents

C Performance Task I
Shapes at Home

Name

I Listen to your teacher.

The world is full of shapes. You can find shapes in the classroom. You can find shapes on the playground. And you can find shapes at home. Let's look at some shapes you might see at home.

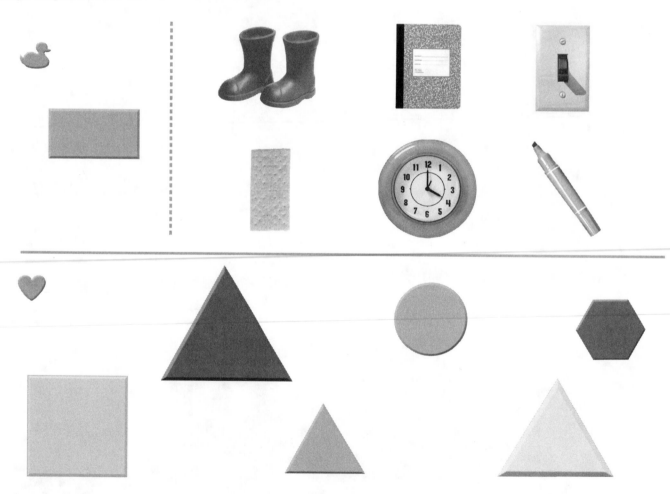

Directions

🦆 Circle the objects that are shaped like the object at the beginning of the row.

❤️ Circle the objects that are the same shape.
Put an X on the objects that are small.

2 Listen to your teacher.

Mr. Lewis has a workbench in his garage. He likes to make wooden shapes. He saws. He hammers. Sometimes he puts pieces together to make new shapes.

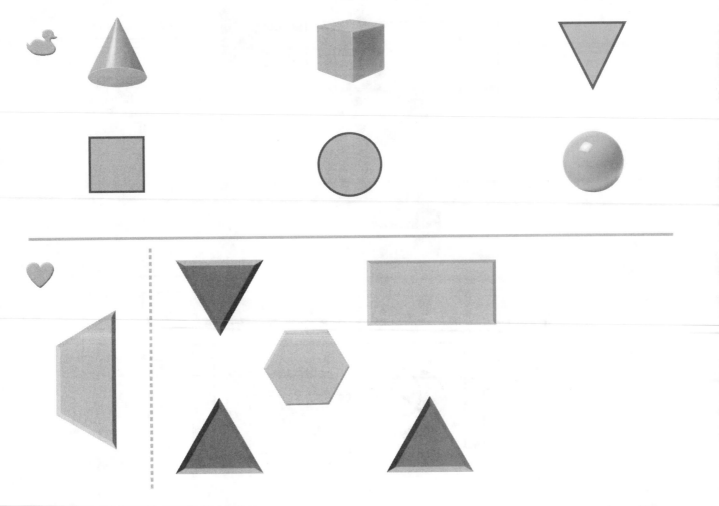

Directions

🦆 Circle the solid figures and name them. Put an X on the flat figures.

🤍 Circle the shapes that have fewer corners than the shape at the beginning of the row. Join pattern blocks for those shapes to make the shape at the beginning of the row. Trace your new shape.

C Performance Task I
Games with Shapes

Name _____

3 Listen to your teacher.

It is a rainy day. Dan and Trish are playing in the house. Maybe you can join them!

Directions

🦆 Name the shapes. Circle the shapes that are beside the box. Put an X on the shape in front of the box.

💜 Name the shapes. Circle the objects below the table. Put an X on the objects above the table.

238 Performance Task I

C Performance Task 1
Backyard Fun

Name _____

4 Listen to your teacher.

The sun is shining. Dan and Trish play in the backyard. They find many things. But how many? You can help them count to find how many.

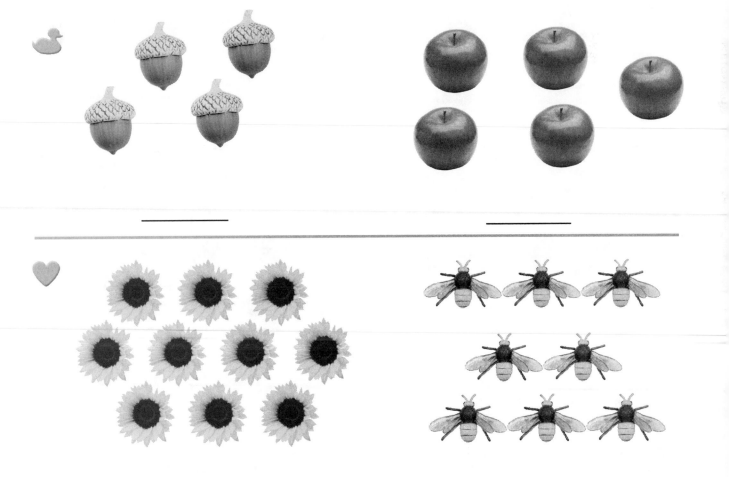

_____   _____

_____   _____

Directions

🦆 Count the acorns. Write the number that tells how many. Count the apples.
Write the number that tells how many. Circle the number that is greater.

💜 Count the flowers. Count the bees. Write the numbers that tell how many.
Circle the number that is less.

C Performance Task 1
Acorn Puzzles

Name _____

5 Listen to your teacher.

Trish and Dan collect some acorns and bring them inside. They make their own number puzzles.

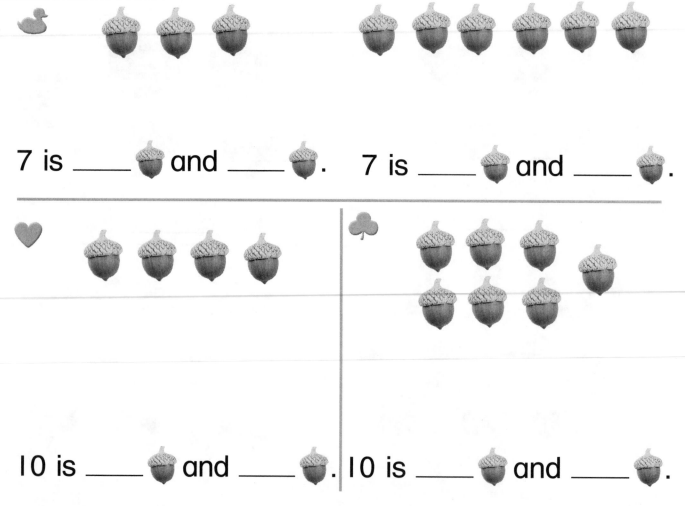

7 is ____ 🌰 and ____ 🌰.   7 is ____ 🌰 and ____ 🌰.

10 is ____ 🌰 and ____ 🌰.   10 is ____ 🌰 and ____ 🌰.

Directions

🦆 Write the numbers to show how to break apart 7 into two parts. Show two different ways.

♥♣ Draw more acorns to make 10. Write the number for each part.

1 Listen to your teacher.

Luis and his friends are at the park. They see many animals to count.

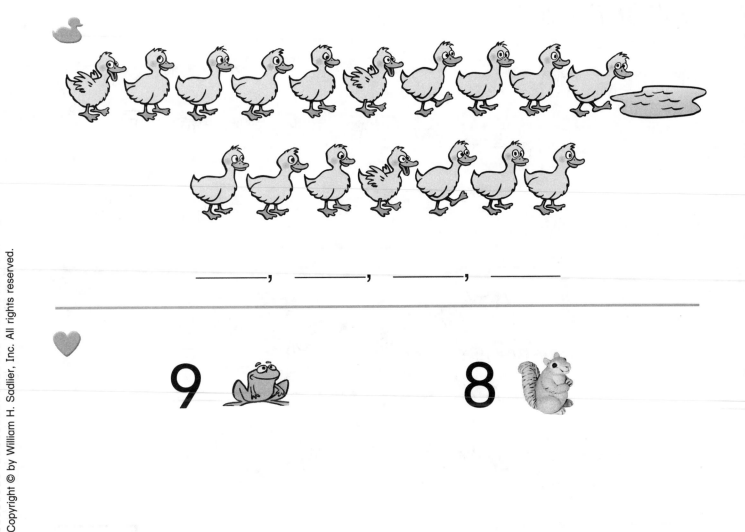

_____ , _____ , _____ , _____

9 🐸   **8** 🐿️

Directions

🦆 Count the ducks. Write the number that tells how many.
Then count forward to 20.

♥ Use counters. Count out the numbers shown. Draw circles
to show the numbers. Then circle the greater number.

Name _____

2 Listen to your teacher.

The children find an anthill. The ants are very busy. The children watch and count the ants. But the children do not bother the ants!

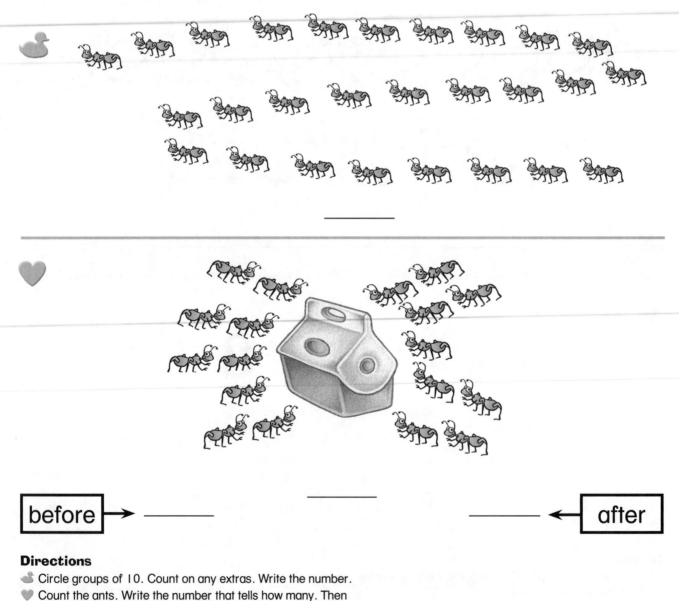

_____

before ⟶ _____ _____   _____ _____ ⟵ after

Directions

🦆 Circle groups of 10. Count on any extras. Write the number.

💜 Count the ants. Write the number that tells how many. Then write the number that comes just before. Then write the number that comes just after.

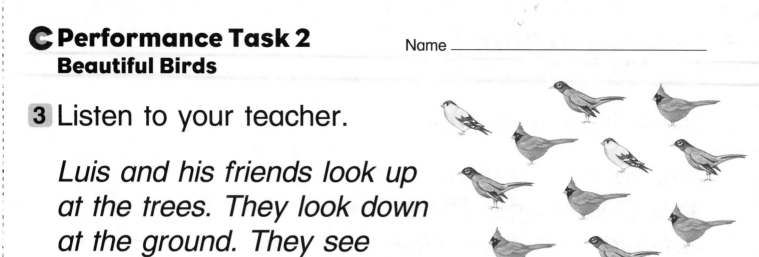

3 Listen to your teacher.

Luis and his friends look up at the trees. They look down at the ground. They see different kinds of birds.

Park Birds			
Bird			
Tally			

_____ ,   _____ ,   _____

Park Birds				

Directions

Count the birds. Draw tally marks to show how many of each kind. Count your tally marks. Write the number next to each bird.

Use your tally chart to make a pictograph. Draw one 🙂 for each tally mark.

Name _____

4 Listen to your teacher.

*Inez looks at a plant. She
sees 2 ladybugs. Three more
ladybugs join them. How
many ladybugs are there?*

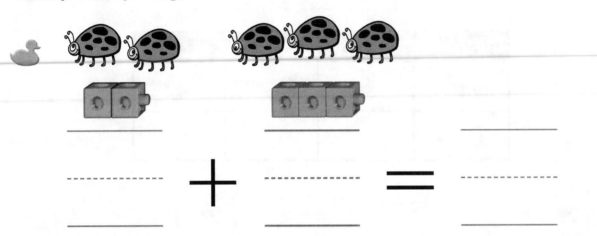

_____   _____   _____

_____ **+** _____ **=** _____

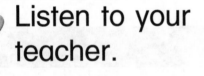 Listen to your
teacher.

*Inez and Luis
see these bees
near a flower.*

_____

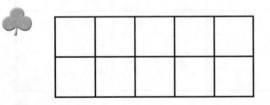

Directions

👆 Model the story with connecting cubes. Write the
number in each part. Then write how many in all.

♥ Count the bees to tell how many. Write the number.

♣ Use the ten-frame. Draw counters to show the number
of bees. Write how many more to make the number.

_____ **=** 10 **+** _____

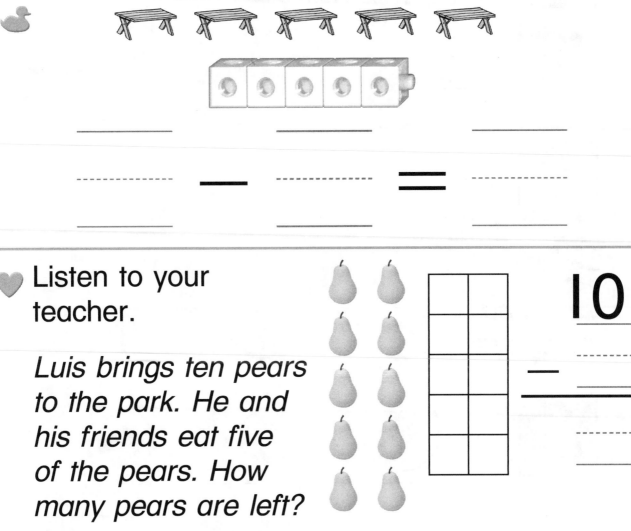
5 Listen to your teacher.

The children are hungry. It is time for lunch. There are five picnic tables. The children sit at four of the tables. How many tables are left?

_____ _____ _____

- - - - - - - - — - - - - - - - - = - - - - - - -

_____ _____ _____

♥ Listen to your teacher.

Luis brings ten pears to the park. He and his friends eat five of the pears. How many pears are left?

10

—

- - - - - - -

- - - - - - -

Directions

🦆 Model the story with connecting cubes. Cross out the part you take away. Write the subtraction. Then write how many are left.

♥ Draw counters in the ten-frame to show the number of pears Luis brings. Cross out the part you take away. Write how many counters you take away. Then write how many are left.

C Performance Task 3
A Trip to the Big Store

Name_____

1 Listen to your teacher.

Three friends go to the big store. Tim takes his money. Bill takes his money. And Gina takes her money.

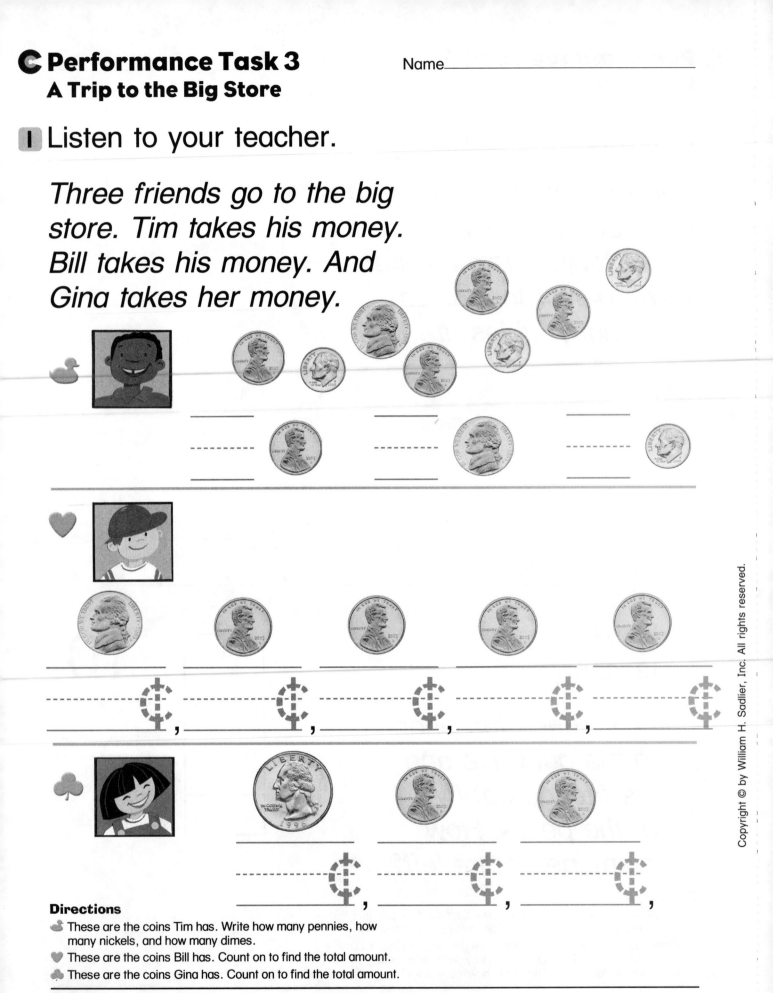

Directions

🦆 These are the coins Tim has. Write how many pennies, how many nickels, and how many dimes.

💜 These are the coins Bill has. Count on to find the total amount.

♣ These are the coins Gina has. Count on to find the total amount.

246 Performance Task 3

Copyright © by William H. Sadlier, Inc. All rights reserved.

C Performance Task 3
What Date Is It?

Name _____

2 Listen to your teacher.

The children see a calendar on the wall at the big store. Tim says, "Hey, tomorrow is Sunday. Yesterday was Friday."

January

Sunday	Monday	Tuesday	Wednesday	Thursday	Friday	Saturday
		1	2	🚗	- - - -	- - - -
6	7	- - - -	🚀		- - - -	12
🚂	14	- - - -	- - - -	- - - -	18	19
- - - -	- - - -	🛸	23	🛸	25	- - - -
27	- - - -	- - - -	30	🚀		

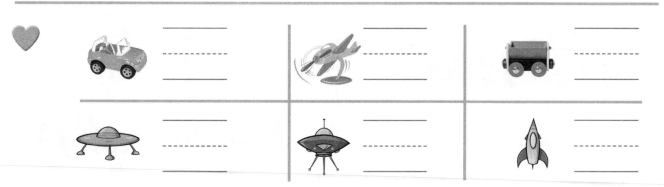

Directions
🦆 Write the missing numbers to complete the calendar.
💜 Write the number for the date each toy is seen.

Performance Task 3 **247**

C Performance Task 3
Taller, Longer, Shorter

Name _____

3 Listen to your teacher.

Tim, Bill, and Gina walk around the big store. They look at items for sale. You can help them compare the sizes of some items.

Directions

🦆 ♥ Circle the picture that is taller.

♣ 🦋 Circle the picture that is longer.

★ ✿ Put an **X** on the picture that is shorter.

248 Performance Task 3

4 Listen to your teacher.

*The big store sells many
things. It sells heavy things and
light things. It sells things that
can hold a lot and things that
can hold a little. The children
like going to the big store.*

Directions: Think about these real objects.

🦆 ❤️ Circle the object that is heavier.

♣️ 🦋 Put an X on the object that holds less.

⭐ Circle an object if you could measure how much it weighs.
Put an X on an object if you could measure how much it holds.
Put a ✔ on an object if you could measure how long it is.

C Performance Task 3
Lots of Balloons

Name _____

5 Listen to your teacher.

*At last, Tim, Bill, and Gina
find what they want—balloons.
The big store sells one hundred
different kinds of balloons!*

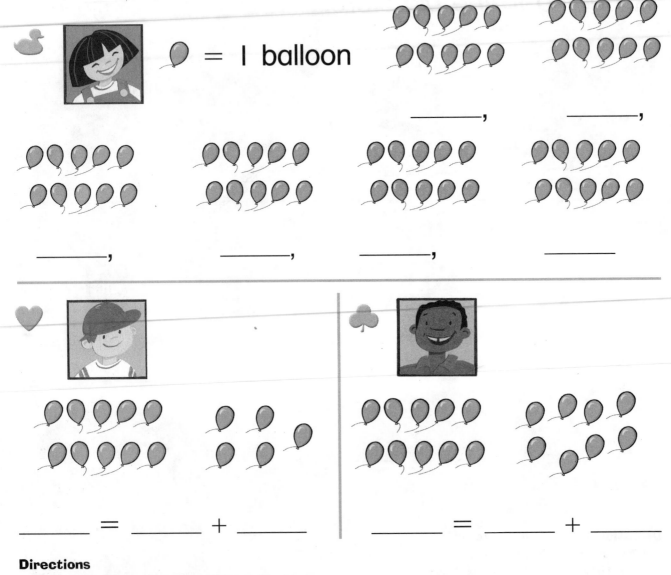

= I balloon

_____ ,   _____ ,

_____ ,   _____ ,   _____ ,   _____

_____ = _____ + _____

_____ = _____ + _____

Directions

Count by 10s to tell how many balloons Gina buys.

Count the balloons the child buys. Write the number as a group of 10 and some more.